SONGS
OF THE
SEA

MC GRAW-HILL BOOK COMPANY

NEW YORK ST. LOUIS SAN FRANCISCO
MONTREAL SAO PAULO TORONTO

STAN HUGILL

SONGS
OF THE
SEA

THE TALES AND TUNES
OF SAILORS AND SAILING SHIPS

CONTENTS

A McGraw-Hill Co-Publication

Copyright © 1977 by McGraw-Hill Book Co. (UK)
Ltd., Maidenhead, England. All rights reserved.

No part of this publication may be reproduced,
stored in a retrieval system, or transmitted in any
form or by any means, electronic, mechanical, photo-
copying, recording, or otherwise, without the prior
written permission of the publisher.

Library of Congress Cataloging in Publication Data
Main entry under title:

Songs of the sea.

  Unacc. melodies.
  Bibliography.
  Discography.
  Includes index.
  1. Sea songs. I. Hugill, Stan.
M1977.S2S68   784.6'8'387   77-7472
ISBN 0-07-031138-2

Photolithography by:
FOTO-LITHO HEGO AG, LITTAU
Switzerland

Composition by:
HERTIG & CO. AG, BIEL
Switzerland

  Song verses handwritten by:
  FRANZ CORAY
  Notes drawn by:
  ERNST HOFER

Printed by:
HERTIG & CO. AG, BIEL
Switzerland

Bound by:
H. + J. SCHUMACHER AG, BERN
Switzerland

Printed in Switzerland

HISTORICAL INTRODUCTION

Part fact, part fantasy, this eighteenth-century view of a disaster at sea was an illustration in Buffon's scientific, encyclopedic Histoire naturelle. *If the dimensions were way off, at least the shape of the "monster" was factual.*

Right: *Landing in a rich West Indies port of call. From a 1590 painting.*

Landsmen have always considered seafarers to be a race apart – almost a different species. From time immemorial seamen have been invested with an aura of mystique. And no wonder! Throughout the ages they have returned home with unbelievable tales – tales of the men of *Ui Breasail* (Hy Brasil) with eyes in their bellies; the Enchanted Isles of the Lotus Eaters; the Kraken in its Maelstrom; the multi-shaped Charybdis and Scylla of the Middle Sea; and mermaids, sirens, and Lorelei whose weird singing would turn a man to stone.

From the days of the Sea-rovers – the Norsemen, Saxons, Jutes, and so on – the gulf between landsmen and seamen has widened perceptibly, at least until modern mechanical times. Once a boy had joined a ship, whether a Viking longship, one of Columbus's caravels, or just a Baltic timber drogher, he soon became a stranger to his shore mates. He learned ways and customs and a language belonging essentially to the sea. There was little difference between the Anglo-Saxon *seafardinger* and the Latin *marinero* in his daily life at sea. His sleeping place, at different periods, was a pallet of straw, a hammock, or a rough wooden bunk. At sea his food was salted beef or fish, coarse

rye bread or biscuit, with a noticeable absence of health-giving vitamins such as those found in green stuffs, milk, fruit, and eggs; hence he suffered a lot from scurvy and other vitamin-deficiency diseases. Damp gave him rheumatism and allied afflictions, while constant hauling and heaving produced more hernias among his kind than among any similar body of men ashore. Although in later years some banes were eliminated – such as scurvy – in the main the life of a seaman in a Cape Horn saltpeterman of the nineteenth century was little different from that of one of Vasco da Gama's seamen.

While the Northern sea-coney, with the exception of those hardy few who roamed the Arctic wastes, sailed mainly the North and Baltic Seas, the mariners of the Mediterranean, on information given them by the wide-ranging Basques, breached the Pillars of Hercules, seeking new lands to the south and west of Europe. The Northern seamen, who navigated with keen eyesight, dead reckoning, and the leadline, scorned the "sheepskins," as they derisively called the *portolanos,* or charts, of their Latin rivals. During the fifteenth and sixteenth centuries, however, among the Genoese, Venetians, Catalans, and Portingals, deepwater ships came into use and navigational aids were developed – these latter mainly by exiled Alexandrian Jews who had taken up residence in Majorca. The caravels of Portugal and of Spain found their various ways to the Azores, along the reef-studded West Coast of Guinea, to the Bahamas, and around the Cape of Storms. During the fifteenth and

sixteenth centuries the ships and seamen of Portugal and Catalan outshone those of all other European nations. Then the Hollanders took over. In this race for maritime power the earliest Dutch ships engaged in the Spitzbergen (called East Greenland) whaling trade, setting up their headquarters in a place called Smeerenberg. From here, too, they sought that new "open sesame" – a passage to the Orient – a route sought by every seafaring nation in Europe.

Following the single-masted *kogge* of the Hanseatic ports came the high charged carracks and sleeker caravels of the Mediterranean and the onion-shaped *fluyts* of Hoorn in Holland, with the galleon of both Latin and English mariners extending still further the discovery of the world. The cutting down of the high-charged and ornamental poop; the use of three masts instead of one; the making of the underbodies of hulls in (to quote the English naval architect Matthew Baker) a "cod's head, mackerel tail" shape; the setting of tops'ls and t'gallants'ls above the single lower sail on each mast; the use of sails on the bowsprit; and the introduction of triangular stays'ls to balance the lateen mizen – all these were high-

Two sixteenth-century approaches to sea cartography: "Sea Monsters of the North Sea" (left), with Norway at the left and Iceland at top; and a Portu- *guese cartographer's study of the Mediterranean* (right), *published 1569 in Venice, one of the first sea charts printed by copper engraving, the pro-*

lights in the development of the deepwater ship. The invention of the cross-staff, backstaff, astrolabe, and octant aided navigation and ousted the unsatisfactory quadrant with its plumbline – useless when trying to get a fix on a heaving deck. The development of better waggoners, or sea-charts, by the Dutchman Wagenaer, and *routiers* by the French (replacing the old Latin *portolanos*), and in Amalfi, Italy, the big stride taken from lodestone to compass-card compasses, all aided the mariner in his work.

Many evils remained, however. The *Role d'Oleron*, the sea-code of ancient Rhodes, now embalmed in the Black Book of Admiralty, still permitted flogging, flogging round the fleet, and keelhauling. Water had to be carried in casks and wooden tanks, which after many days at sea became the home of germs breeding "ship fever" (typhus) and many other vicious contagions. Once illness hit a ship it soon swept through the fleet, since all exploratory and commercial ships of the sixteenth, seventeenth, and eighteenth centuries, on account of pirates and privateers, sailed in companies and fleets. The fleet of the Frenchman Dubois de la Motte, returning home from a voyage to Canada in 1757, entered Brest with 6,000 cases of typhus aboard his ships; the disease spread in no time to the shore population. The English seaman Anson lost eighty of his men through scurvy in the South Pacific in 1741.

With the exception of coasting vessels, all merchant ships were armed to the teeth and all seamen were trained to be fighting men. The English (1601) and the Dutch (1602) East Indiamen were the first deepwater merchant ships and they were heavily armed; their crews trained in naval fashion and they sailed in convoys. With the demise of these ships – the French Indiamen in 1770 becoming units of the French navy, the Dutch and English Indiamen petering out from 1832 onward – lone, less-armed ships of commerce began to cross the ocean trade routes. The period from the beginning of the seventeenth century to the middle of the eighteenth has been called the Age of Adventure. It was an age of filibusters, buccaneers, and pirates, of privateersmen and non-scientific seamen. They scoured the globe, proselytizing or marauding, seeking converts, gold, and commercial openings. Cartography was a secret weapon then. The Dutch guarded their East Indian routes under pain of death, the Portuguese threatened torture to revealers of the contents of their charts, and the Frenchman Bougainville refused pointblank to give the exact position of the newly-found island of Tahiti.

From this period of our history – the fifteenth to the eighteenth century – what knowledge have we of the songs of the mariner? As far as literary research goes our earliest

cess that dominated maritime chart printing until the twentieth century. The engraving was large and accurate enough to be useful at sea.

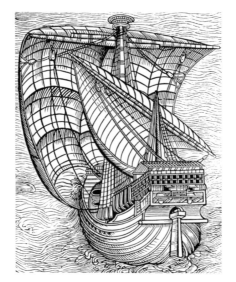

inkling of sailors singing at work comes from a manuscript of the reign of the English king Henry VI (1421–71). This is a sea ballad – perhaps the oldest in Europe – describing a ship loaded with pilgrims, bound from Sandwyche, Wynchelsee, and Bristow (Bristol) toward the shrine of St. James (Santiago) in Compostella, Spain. Those who are interested will find the full ballad in *The Early Naval Ballads of England* in the library of Trinity College, Cambridge. In quaint Chaucerian English the ballad covers the sailing day, the type of food and sleeping quarters allotted to the pilgrims, their sea-sickness, a description of the *schipp-hlaford* (master) and his men, the orders given when getting their anchors and setting sail, and, for the first time, a mention of the wild yell – the "hitch" – sailors have used from earliest times when hauling on a rope.

The first reference to the singing of work songs while pulling on a rope – what later seamen called "shantying" – and to a lead-singer – the "shantyman" of later years – is to be found in the work of a Dominican friar, Felix Fabri of Ulm, Germany, who in 1493 sailed aboard a Venetian galley to Palestine. Shantymen are described as "mariners who sing when work is going on.... [There is] a concert between one who sings out orders and the laborers who sing in response." The earliest source giving a series of work songs (without tunes) sung at sea is called *The Complaynt of Scotland* (1549), by Barbour. Two anchor songs are given, one bowline shanty, and three hauling songs for hoisting the lower yard; all very

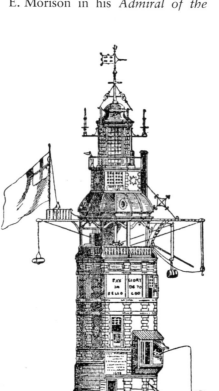

much like those sung by seamen in my day – apart from the archaic lingo!

From 1550 until the early 1800s, English-worded shanties (and those of other European seamen too) seem to have disappeared from the shipboard scene. However, Samuel E. Morison in his *Admiral of the*

Ocean Sea (1942) refers to an ancient Spanish shanty sung aboard Columbus's ships, and Luiz de Camoens, in his *Luciades* (1572), tells us it was the custom aboard the ships of Vasco da Gama's fleet, en route to India, for the sailors to "sing songs and catches to lighten their work," when raising their anchors and making sail.

A certain Mr. Forrest, in *A Voyage to New Guinea* (1775), writes that "the Moors in what is called country ships in East India, have

also their cheering songs at work in hoisting, or in their boats a rowing." Country ships were built in India and Burma, traded the Indian Ocean, and very often had English officers and lascar (East Indian) crews. The fact that such work songs were called "cheering songs" shows that English, or a mixture of Anglo-Hindustani, was used as the lingua franca, the only reference in print to English-worded shanties being used in the eighteenth century. Whereas in the Age of Adventure Dutch was the lingua franca of Northern seamen, and Spanish that of Southern seamen, from the eighteenth century onward, because sailing-ship crews were so cosmopolitan, all orders were given in English or a Pidgin English.

The reason usually given for the demise of the shanty in English ships during the seventeenth and eighteenth centuries was the press-

ganging of merchant seamen into the "King's Navee," leaving the merchant fleet to be manned by foreigners to whom shantying was, as far as we know, unknown. Then again, perhaps shantying died out on account of the small ships and large crews. By the nineteenth century the axiom was "big ships, small crews," hence the shantyman became "worth ten men on a rope." In the navies of the world all work was done in time with numbers and with the bosun's call or pipe. Singing at work was taboo.

Even sailorsongs of leisure from

adorn them with tunes from other folksongs, but this does not give us a song as it was actually mouthed by wine-bibbing sea-coneys in a sailortown tavern in the eighteenth century.

Jullen, kom Gesvint!" A variant of the first song is said to have been used by Puccini in his opera *Manon Lescaut*.

France, too, can produce some from the days of Louis XIII (1601–43), Louis XIV (1638–1715), and from the eighteenth century: "Chansons pour Passer le Temps," "Les Filles de Camaret," "Sur les Bords de la Loire," "La Fille de Sables," and "La Corsairienne" (a rowing song). And here are a few titles of genuine eighteenth-century (and even earlier) English seasongs: "The Dolphin," "The Coasts of Barbaree,"

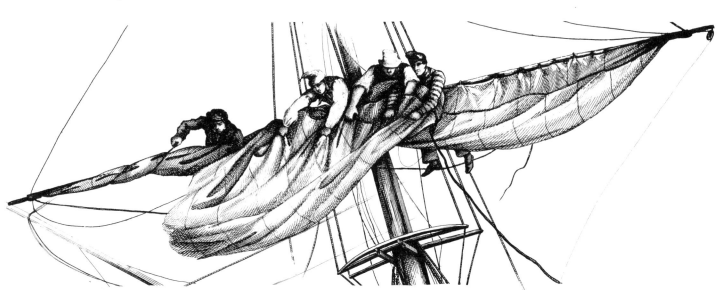

these early centuries are difficult to find. There do exist many dusty tomes in world libraries containing collections of so-called seasongs, mainly without airs, but most of these were composed by broadside-ballad makers on shore, and rarely, if ever, sung by seamen. There is a tendency in modern folkclubs to dig out the better of these "poems" — for that is what they are — and

Research suggests that genuine old German and Dutch seasongs – of the seventeenth and eighteenth centuries – have not survived the tide of time. In Sweden, however, they have done better. Here are the titles of a few from the eighteenth century: "Flickorna i Rotterdam," "Här Blåser Nordost," "Då Vi Kommer ut i en Svarter Natt," "Bramråvisan," and "Kom med

"Captain Ward," "The New York Trader," "The Golden Vanitee," "Bold Benbow," "The Lowlands of Holland," "Cartagena," "The Nightingale," "The Old Ramillies," "Jack Tar," and "On Board a Man-o'-War."

With this short introduction we will now look at the prime period of sailorsong and shanty – the nineteenth century.

THE AGE OF SAIL AND SONGS 1818-1920s

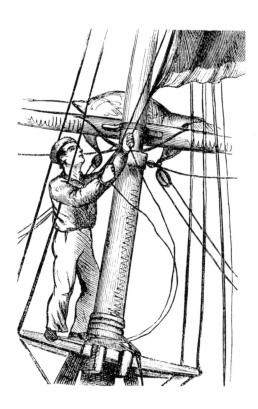

Danish sailor aloft, loosening the ropes of a tops'l in preparation for the setting of the sail.

With the end of the Napoleonic Wars and the growing effect of the Industrial Revolution, the great desire throughout Europe and America was for speed; merchants and industrialists urged marine architects and ship-owners to produce faster ships. The days of the bluff-bowed, pot-bellied East Indiamen were coming to an end; masters had to relinquish their outmoded methods of ship-handling and adjust to the newer form of seamanship. By the fifties the days of "carrying on" and "what she can't carry she can drag" had arrived.

The old-time seamen so beloved of novelists were, to quote Captain A. H. Clark, "coarse, vulgar, ignorant men, full of lurid oaths, their persons emitting an unpleasant odour of cheap rum and stale tobacco...unable to speak or write their own language with any degree of correctness...good sailors...but, their knowledge and ambition limited to dead reckoning, the tar-bucket and marlinspike...with no desire to master the higher branches of navigation." The transition to the newer type, obviously, took some time. The milestones in this development were the winding up of the East India Companies (British and Dutch) from 1832 onward, allowing ships of other firms into the lucrative India and China trade; the founding of Lloyd's Registry of Shipping (1834) to provide a proper survey and classification of merchant ships; and the final Repeal of the Navigation Acts (1849).

In 1818 the famous Blackball line, renowned in song and legend, put its fast packet ships on bimonthly schedules between New York and Liverpool, something never heard of before. They were soon followed by the ships of other packet firms – Swallowtail, Dramatic, Black Cross, and Red Star lines. Hard on the heels of the East Indiamen, but not following the latter's nightly custom of sending down masts and yards so as to be "snug for the night," came the so-called Blackwall frigates of Green, Wigram, and Dunbar. They were engaged in the Orient trade, but were soon superseded – in the late 1840s and 50s – by the newly arrived clippers.

Most agree that the first real clipper was the American ship *Rainbow* of 1843. The California goldrush of 1848 stimulated the need for speed and soon fast American clippers were racing round Cape Horn bound for Frisco. Other American clippers were put on the China-tea run, soon to be followed by fast British composite clippers. The American clippers were of wood,

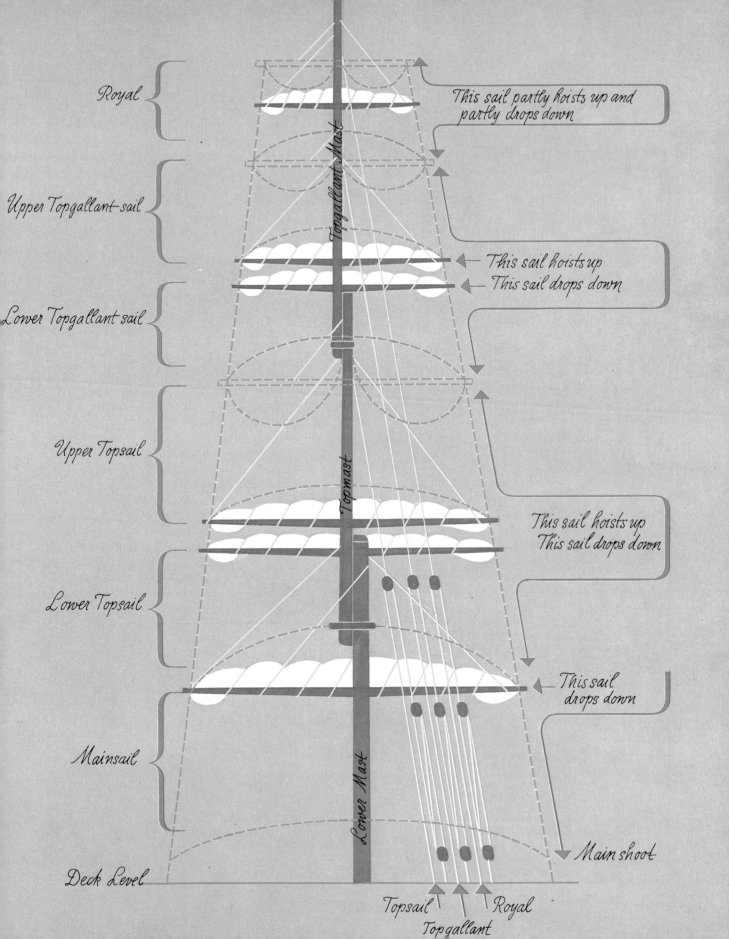

Royal

Upper Topgallant-sail

Lower Topgallant sail

Upper Topsail

Lower Topsail

Mainsail

Deck Level

Topgallant Mast

Topmast

Lower Mast

This sail partly hoists up and partly drops down

This sail hoists up
This sail drops down

This sail hoists up
This sail drops down

This sail drops down

Main shoot

Topsail   Royal
Topgallant

the British with iron frames and wooden skins. Such ships carried "flying kites" – skysails, moonsails, stuns'ls (stretched beyond the standard sails), Jimmie Greens (under the bowsprit), ringtails (abaft the spanker), save-alls (between the foot of one square sail and the head of the next), and water-sails (over the ship's sides). Competition was the thing and every part of a ship was designed for speed. With the opening of the Suez Canal steamships going out East became the sailing ship's rival and many of the tea clippers dropped out of the China trade and began carrying wool and gold from Australia and emigrants (1860s) outward.

The shanty was the work song of the sailor and the forebitter his song of leisure; both came into being about the 1830s (although some forebitters are older). Shanties, as far as we know, were born in the period between 1830 and 1860, but on account of some of the big crews these packet and clipper ships carried, they were probably not used to the same extent as they were in ships of the latter part of the century. These ships of the seventies,

eighties, and nineties were mainly of iron – big ships, barks, and four-masted barks engaged in the grain trade from Frisco, the wool and wheat trade from Australia, and the nitrate trade from the Chile coast; ships of 2,000 tons with small crews of thirty or fewer hands. So it is correct to say that although the shanty was born in the period 1830–60, it really came into general use only toward the end of the century.

In the nineteenth century young sailors, both merchant seamen and whalermen, came from all walks of society, but within no time they were molded into true sons of Neptune. There was little difference between the sailormen of Britain, America, Germany, Holland, France, and Scandinavia; the sea put its mark on each one of them. Dressing any of them in the rig of a clergyman would never obliterate

the hallmarks of a real deep-water seaman. In the last century and the early years of this one, the "rig" of the sailormen of all countries consisted of a jersey, dungaree trousers and jacket, and a woollen cap, with leather or rubber seaboots (in high latitudes) and rope-yarn slippers (in the tropics). Add to this his belt and sheath-knife and suit of oilskins and you have a fairly representative picture of a well-dressed seaman. Bosuns, "chippys" (carpenters), and sailmakers would wear soft-crowned peak-caps, and very often a double-breasted serge jacket. Heavier pea jackets would be worn by all in cold weather. In dirty weather "soul 'n' body lashings" would be added. These consisted of the belt and sheath-knife being put outside the oilskin jacket, a rope-yarn under the crotch from the front of the belt to the back of the belt, rope-yarn lashings around each cuff and below the knees – like a navvy's "boweyangs" – and a rope-yarn from the back of the sou'wester to the belt (to prevent the hat blowin' off when aloft). All these were to keep "body and soul" together in Cape Horn weather and

The bluff-bowed, potbellied East Indiamen (here and on facing page) were, by

the 1850s, becoming obsolete as the demand for speed became all-important.

None of the lighter craft shown at left would have been called a ship in the last century.

would sometimes be worn for two months without being taken off. Each man helped his neighbor to put them on. The result of wearing these lashings so long, and even sleeping in them, was that saltwater boils and cuts would appear on a man's wrists and neck caused by the chafing and the cold. A towel would be put around the neck as a scarf.

The fo'c'sle wherein the men lived would, in earlier days, be up under the fo'c'sle-head within the V formed by the bows, or else it would be a deckhouse abaft the foremast. In later ships it was in a cross-sectional "bridge" amidships known as a "Liverpool house." Double rows of bunks would line the walls, and in the earlier fo'c'sle the anchor chains, slimy and smelling, would swing between the bunks from the navel-pipes above to the chain-locker beneath. Food was eaten in the earlier ships sitting on one's sea-chest, in later ships from wooden tables with wooden bars called "fiddles" jammed across them to stop the plates sliding as the ship rolled.

The seaman naturally spoke a lingo all his own, and the young lads had

to pick it up. There was rarely any tuition given by the older seamen to the younger; the latter had to acquire the sailorly arts by observation, very few old-timers being willing to impart their esoteric knowledge to first-trippers. The lads would receive plenty of cuffs and blows from the old-timers during their "green years." This "discipline" was even more severe in German and French ships than in British. In such ships an A.B. (able-bodied seaman) would constantly remind a youngster that he was inferior. In German ships a deckboy *(licht Matrosen)* had to pull an A.B.'s seaboots off, fill and light his pipe, and generally attend to the older man's wants. These "prime" A.B.s took a great pride in their work and virtually kept a "closed shop" when it came to letting others in on their trade secrets. Seamen weren't, in the main, game-minded, unless you can call it a game to race

weevils (from the biscuits) up the afore-mentioned tables, prompting them with pins, the stake being plugs of hard tobacco.

Superstitions were many among these seamen of the sail (see pages 180 ff.). On the whole sailors weren't religious in the orthodox sense, but they did have a sort of natural religion. The old-timer had his own hierarchy of gods – Davy Jones (probably a form of Duffy Jonas; i.e., the ghost of Jonah) and his wife Mother Carey (probably the Roman Mater Cara) ruled in the Big Locker, beneath the seas, whereas Neptune ruled *above* the seas. The little seabird known as a stormy petrel was nicknamed by seamen "Mother Carey's chicken" and was thought to be a member of the court of Davy Jones and a harbinger of stormy weather. The word "petrel" comes from St. Peter who, like Mother Carey's chickens, "walks" upon the water.

During the latter part of the nineteenth century, sailing-ship voyages were mainly on the following routes: the Colonies (Australia and New Zealand) for wool and grain; New Caledonia for nickel-ore;

More Indiamen, shown in their days of glory (early nineteenth century).

A battle in the Indian Ocean between French and East Indian ships, 1804.

China with case-oil from America; Newcastle, N.S.W., to Callao with coal; outward from Europe with coal, coke, and timber (from the Baltic) to various parts of the world; from the West Coast of North America with grain and timber; and to the West Coast of South America for guano and saltpeter. Outward and homeward passages to such places would each take three to four months, and most ships only made one round voyage a year.

Ships engaged in the Chilean nitrate trade were mainly British, German, and French. Leaving a continental port on a typical passage to Chile (perhaps with a cargo of coal or steel rails), the ships would normally have to beat their way down Channel against a sou'west wind, or else they would go north about,

The word "trade," when referring to winds, has nothing to do with trading but comes from a Saxon word for "path" or "way."

In wintertime, until the northeast trade was picked up, somewhere about the latitude of the Azores, the going would be tough aboard these old square-riggers. Down Channel, braces would be manned continuously, often in rain and hail squalls with a choppy sea. The men would all be strangers to each other, and often to the ship as well. It was a period of settling down and getting to know the afterguard. Upper sails would be taken in quite often and men who had joined the ship without oilskins and seaboots would have a rough time of it. In some ships the captain ran a "slop-chest," which would be opened the first Sunday at sea and these unfortu-

became more pleasant and men would air and wash their salt-encrusted gear, dry out and air their "donkey's breakfasts" (straw paillasses) and blankets and get down to hobbies such as making model ships and putting ships in bottles. It was the time for "fufu bands" (homemade instruments) and sing-songs on the fo'c'slehead – on the capstan and forebitts – in mild weather. As the trades were entered a change of sails would be the job, the hard-weather canvas being unbent and sent below to the locker, and the tropic gear sent aloft. The latter would be worn and patched.

Around the equator between the northeast and southeast trades were the doldrums and flat calms. A ship could sometimes lay for weeks in this sweltering area awaiting a puff

hoping for a fair wind to take them out into the Atlantic via the Orkneys. The sails used at this time would be their best canvas, known to French seamen as *la chemise de bonne sœur*, "the shift of the good sisters," equivalent to a hair shirt. Somewhere off the Portuguese coast they would hope to pick up a false northeast trade wind known as the *Nortado* or the Portuguese trades.

nates allowed to buy from it "heavy gear" for the Cape Horn passage, the cost being deducted from their wages at the end of the voyage. Life in the fo'c'sle at such times was miserable. With the four-hours-on and four-hours-off watch system, when a man left the deck his bunk was the only warm, dry place in which to rest himself.

Upon reaching the trades, life

of wind. Braces were hauled continuously for the sails to catch the least tremor of wind, and rain squalls would fill the deck with fresh water. Men would strip off and bathe themselves, perhaps the only decent all-over wash they would have on the journey, and they would wash their clothes as well. Catching sharks, bonito, alba-core, and barracuda from the jib-

Below left: *New York harbor, 1717: view of Manhattan Island from the Brooklyn shore.*

Ship's boy being trained to become an "A.B." – able-bodied seaman.

Below center: *Figurehead of the* Ajax, *built at Blackwall in 1809.*

boom was one pastime; and in a deeply laden ship, a hurricane lamp placed on deck near an open washport would invite flying fish to wing their way aboard – a welcome change from salt meat!

Once through the southeast trades and the variables, the ship would prepare herself for the battle with Cape Horn – Cape Stiff to the Britisher, *Kap Hoorn* to the German and Dutchman, and *Cap Dur* to the French *matelot*. Homeward bound the "brave west wind" at the Horn helped the ship on her way, but outward bound it was a dead muzzler, causing sailors to use such expressions as "clawing our way to wind'ard," "a stiff beat around ol' Stiff," and "a back-stay passage round the Horn." The ship would have to beat as far as 60°S on one tack, then head upward toward the

middle of the night, usually, the cry would come: "All hands! In main upper tops'l!" – and the watch below would stumble bleary-eyed from their warm bunks, seizing an opportunity to open the deckhouse door in between great seas crashing aboard, and as often as not plunge knee-deep into icy water. In the pitch dark, downhauls and buntlines would be hauled on, the hal-

yards slackened, and the braces attended to. Wild sing-outs accompanied the hauling. Aloft, up the weather rigging, the wind flattened the men against the shrouds, up and over the futtock shrouds, bodies hanging virtually over the sea as the ship rolled to wind'ard. The top of the rigging, perhaps covered with ice, could easily cause a man to slip and drop into the sea – with no chance of being picked up in such weather. Then up the twisting topmast shrouds, followed by a leap from the topmast shrouds to the footrope of the tops'l yard, across the inky gap between the two. Crablike, the men would shuffle outward along the two-inch footrope in the Stygian darkness, with the sail bellying dangerously backward over the yard. With frozen fists the men now pummeled the

Horn, 58°S, on the next leg. A look at used sea-charts of Cape Horn voyages shows, in many cases, a real criss-cross network of ship's tracks between the Horn and the South Shetlands, covering Drake Passage, often showing that the ship had been beaten backward.

Shortening sail in a full Cape Horn snifter was a terrible physical effort for everyone concerned. In the

canvas to flatten the wind out of it; then, seizing icy folds as hard as wood, they tried to get a "skin" and roll the frozen mass up onto the yard. This was done to a sing-out:

Timmy way, hay, high, ya!
We'll pay Paddy Doyle for his boots!

– a concerted roll being made on the wild shout of *boots!* Then the gas-

17

French chart showing sea routes around the dreaded Cape Horn.

kets or rope ties would be passed, one man leaning over the yard and throwing the gasket to another sitting athwart the footrope, until the sail was made fast. Then the watch below would slide down the backstays to get quickly to their bunks, while the watch on deck would take their time to go down the shrouds.

After rounding the Horn the ship would head for the coast of Chile and her order port. From the latter she would proceed to one of the nitrate ports where she would moor in the tiers until her cargo arrived in barges.

Many men deserted in these West Coast ports, went "on the beach" as they called it, dreading another Horn rounding. These ports were full of beachcombers, many becoming heavy vino drinkers to their physical detriment. Crimps and boarding-house masters were well established here and many a ship without a crew was supplied either by willing sailor beachcombers or by doped bodies shanghaied aboard by the crimps. Often the members of such a shanghaied crowd did not know one end of a ship from the

other, being peasants, farmers, office workers or whoever else was foolhardy enough to drink in such dives as the "First and Last," the "Chain Locker," or the "Flags of All Nations."

In days gone by the word *ship* was used to mean solely a three-masted vessel with yards and square sails on all three masts. There were a few four-masted ships and even fewer five-masted ships, each mast having yards and square sails. A three-masted vessel carrying yards on the

front (fore) and middle (main) masts is a *bark*, the last mast (mizzen) being rigged fore 'n' aft; i.e., like a schooner with sails in line with the deck. Then again there is the four-masted bark, with yards on three masts and the last fore 'n' aft. These were more common than any other rig in the eighties and nineties of the last century. Also there was the odd five-masted bark. The criterion in regard to multi-masted barks is that the last mast must carry fore 'n' aft rigging.

A smaller square-rigger was the *brig*, a two-masted vessel bearing yards and square sails on both masts. Such a rig had begun to die out by the 1880s even in the coasting trades, the Mediterranean being their last stronghold. The *snow* was dying out even earlier in the century. She was like a brig but behind the main mast was a slender extra mast to which the fore 'n' aft spanker, driver, or brig sail was laced. A *brigantine* was of two masts only; earlier she had a square sail on both masts — the rig is described in various ways in nautical dictionaries — but by the latter half of the nineteenth century she

American clipper ships (left and right), *winners of races from China, 1860s.*

Center: *British merchantmen shown making for the Thames.*

was rigged with square sails on the foremast and fore 'n' aft gaff sail on the main, with triangular stays'ls between the masts. A *barkentine* was, and is, a three-masted vessel with yards on the foremast and fore 'n' aft gaff sails on the main and mizzen. Actually, in America, there were many multi-masted barkentines early in the present century.

Those are all the recognized classes of square-riggers; every other type of merchant sailing vessel is classed as a *fore 'n' after;* e.g., *tops'l schooners* (with two or three square sails on the foremast), *schooners* (gaff-rigged vessels up to six masts and one freak — a seven-master), *ketches, yawls, sloops,* and so on among the smaller craft. It was aboard square-riggers that shanties were sung, the rig of a fore 'n' after not requiring such work songs.

In order to understand the nautical terminology in the working of a sailing ship of the latter half of the nineteenth century, here is a simplified explanation of those parts of the sails and rigging which normally baffle the landsman.

The masts of a sailing ship are in three parts — *lowermast, topmast,* and *t'gallantmast.* Each mast, like all the gear attached to it, is prefaced by the words *fore, main, mizzen* (or *jigger*), according to its position from the bows of the ship — the fore being that nearest the bow, and the mizzen or jigger being that nearest the stern, depending on whether the vessel is a three- or four-master.

Spars of wood or hollow metal slung horizontally across the masts and to which the square sails are bent (i.e., fastened), are called *yards.* From the two bottom corners of the square sails there are ropes, wires, or chains called *sheets,* which haul down the bottom corners or *clews* of each sail to the yardarms of the yard beneath; the sheets (and tacks) of the lowest sails or *courses* are hauled down to positions on the deck. The upper sheets lead through sheaves in the yardarms, through blocks near the center of each yard (near the mast), and then down to the fiferail at the foot of each mast. The lower ends of these sheets are fitted with strong rope purchases, the hauling parts of which go to belayin' pins in the fiferails.

The sail nearest the deck on the foremast is called the *fore course,* or more commonly by seamen, the *fores'l.* The next sail upward is the *fore lower tops'l* with the *fore upper tops'l* above it. The next would be the *t'gallants'l,* either single or double — *lower and upper t'gallants'l* — with the word "fore" prefaced to each name. The highest sail is the *royal,* although some ships carried a *skysail* above this. With the word *main* or *mizzen* prefacing each of the above sails we have the names of all the square sails in a sailing ship.

The *spanker* is the fore 'n' aft gaff sail on the mizzen or jigger mast. Between all the masts are triangular sails called *stays'ls,* and hoisted up from the spike that sticks out the front of a windship is the *fore topmast stays'l,* with beyond it several more triangular sails called *jibs.* Every sail is hoisted with a *halyard* (a corruption of "haul yard"), and all yards are moved from side to side, according to the direction of the wind, by means of *braces.* Sails are collapsed and pulled up to their respective yards using *buntlines* and *leechlines,* with the corners being

More clipper ships: the Cimber, *a Danish ship* (above); *the* Ariel (center); *and the* Guiding Star, 1853, *bound for Australia. The last two are American.*

19

pulled up by means of ropes called *clewlines*.

A ship is sailed basically in two positions; one, with the wind behind her, *running free* as it is called, when the yards and square sails are at right angles to the masts; and two, with the wind ahead, when the yards are placed at an acute angle to the masts and the ship has to sail in a zigzag fashion either side the wind, called by seamen *tacking* or *beating*. A third position, used when the master wants to stop the ship – to pick up the pilot, say – is that of being *hove to*. In this case the yards of the mainmast are put in a position diametrically opposed to all the others, with the wind pressing them against the mast and so stopping the ship.

All the above-mentioned ropes are moved by Armstrong's Patent – i.e., men's muscle power – but there were also machines of a sort in each ship. These consisted of the *capstan* and/or *windlass*, found on the fo'c'slehead or at the break of the fo'c'slehead, both used for heaving up the anchor and warping a ship through lock gates and docks and so on; the *pumps*, usually situated somewhere near the mainmast, at the fiferail; and in some ships, hand-heaving *cargo winches*, near to the main hatch.

The following classification of sailor work songs is rather arbitrary, since individual seamen and collectors do not always agree as to which job a certain shanty was used for; or to quote a sailor proverb, "Different ships, different long splices, sez the Dutchman as he went aft to hoist the jib."

First there was the *sing-out,* that wild onomatopoeic chant used in hoisting a light headsail, during the initial stages of hoisting a square sail, at braces, or to get a final pull on anything, even in the drawing on of seaboots! The sing-out is historically the lowly beginning from which came the more musical capstan song.

The next type of work song, in historical sequence, would be the *hand-over-hand song,* used when hoisting light fore 'n' afters. Two or three men, in time, would grasp and pull a rope, first in one hand then in the other. In such a chant scat syllables and wild yelps – called by seamen "hitches" – were also used but mixed with more intelligible phrases, such as "Hill-ay-o-o-yu, rise 'er up, me bullies, hill-ay-o-o-yu!" or "Hand, hand, hand over hand, Divil run away a Liverpool man!" and "Do, ray, me, fah, soh, la, ti, doh, What makes me fart I do not know!"

Next, moving toward more musical examples, there is the *sweating-up chants* – brevities, few of which have survived – such as:

You stole me boots, you St. Helena soger,
*You stole me boots – ah-*ha!

– the pull coming on the final *ha!*
A further development was the

short haul song, called by Yankee seamen a *short drag song*. This was sung fairly fast and used on royal halyards and the less heavy square sails:

Boney was a warrior,
Ch.: Way-*aye-yah!*
Oh, Boney was a warrior,
Ch.: John *François!*

The words in roman are where the pulls came; sometimes two pulls would be given in each refrain.

The full flowering of hauling songs is to be found in the *halyard shanties* – mainly theme-possessing four-liners used to hoist tops'ls and t'gallants'ls. To set one of these sails a boy or two would be sent aloft to loose the gaskets or rope ties, and on stepping clear into the rigging they would hail the haulers ready on deck with a loud, "All clear aloft!" The chain or wire pendant of a halyard would run from the center of the yard, through a sheave built into the mast and terminating in a great *gin block* (a block of metal without a proper shell or covering). Over the sheave of this gin block would be the *bight* (center) of a chain, one end shackled to

Three sketches from a collection called The Sailor's Life, *painted in 1881 by*

Youthful seaman doing some repainting – a break in his otherwise rigorous on-job training.

the deck, the other end terminating in a great two-block purchase, each block having three or four sheaves in it, the lower block being shackled to the deck on the opposite side to the other leg of the bight. The hauling part of this purchase, made of hemp or manila, would lead down to the deck and when the sail was ready for hoisting would be led through a *snatch block* – a wooden block with one side hinged so as to allow the bight of the hauling part (the *fall*) to be inserted – and thence along the deck. Where the fall or hauling part came down from aloft, in front of the snatch block, stood the *fore-hand* (the shantyman) and perhaps the bosun or second mate, with their hands well above their heads grasping the rope. The seamen-haulers would string out along the horizontal part of the rope, backs bent as low as possible and not too close to each other – "How the hell can a man pull with you spitting in his bloody ear-'ole?" was a frequent admonition by older hands to the younger seamen.

On the cry of "All clear!" from aloft the shantyman would give a couple of timed sing-outs to take in the slack of the halyard and to shake out the wet sail from its confined folds, caused by being lashed with gaskets. Once the sail caught the wind and bellied free from the yard the shantyman would break forth into his solo, although sometimes, to give the hands notice of the shanty he had in mind, he would first sing the refrain. Yankee seamen called such halyard shanties "long drags."

Shantyman: *A handy ship and a handy crew,*
Refrain: Hand*y me boys, so* handy!
Shantyman: *A handy mate and skipper too,*
Refrain: Hand*y me boys, so* handy!

Another type of rope-hauling shanty was the one known as a *stamp 'n' go song* or *walkaway shanty*. The best known nowadays is "Drunken Sailor." Such songs were only sung in a ship carrying a big crew. The men would grasp the rope with their backs to the block, keeping the rhythm by stamping their feet in march time as they belted out this type of thing:

Way-hay! An' away we go!
Hieland laddie, bonnie laddie!
Way-hay! An' away we go,
Me bonnie hieland laddie O!

These stamp 'n' go songs were often raised at the braces when going "'bout ship" or when wishing to hoist a light sail quickly, or when "marrying the falls"; i.e., putting two ropes together in one's hands, for use when hoisting up a ship's boat from the water. This class of shanty is said to have been the only one ever permitted in the British Navy – and then only in small vessels like revenue cutters.

The final type of rope-hauling shanty is that known to seamen as a *fore-sheet song*. In practice these songs were used not only on fore sheets but were sung at tacks, braces, and even halyards, to get a final inch on an already taut rope. The pull came on the final word of the refrain which was always yelled out and never given its full musical value:

Haul the bowline, for Kitty she's me darlin',
Refrain: *Haul the bowline, the bowline* HAUL!

or:

Oh! Do me Johnny Bowker, come rock 'n' roll me over,
Refrain: *Oh! Do me Johnny Bowker* DO!

Most of the foregoing shanties are four-liners. Other four-liners were those employed at the *windlass* – the antiquated, horizontal-barrel machine dating back to early times and not the great steel or iron

I. Westerfelt on the basis of an outline made by B. A. Wikström; the latter's

firsthand experience at sea presumably lent these scenes their authenticity.

machine of the latter-day windships – situated beneath the fo'c'slehead, which had *gipsies* wherein lay the anchor cable and cable controls and was moved by means of the double-headed capstan on the fo'c'slehead. This windlass was called a *brake-windlass,* usually placed at the break of the fo'c'slehead. The two anchor cables were coiled around its barrel, one to port and one to starboard, the one not in use being slackened and triced up to the strongback above by lengths of rope. The strongback, made of oak, lay across the two great bitts in which the axle of the horizontal barrel, or drum, revolved. In the center of and just behind the drum was another bitt – the *pawl-bitt,* so called because it was fitted with squares of iron (the *pawls*), which contacted a toothed rim in the center of the barrel and prevented the drum going backward at anchor-heaving. The barrel was worked by metal levers called *brakes,* which by a series of connecting rods and cogs, and a rocker head, worked the pawls and thereby turned the barrel and hove the cable inward. To slack the chain on dropping the anchor, the barrel was immovable, and so the cable was slacked around it. In order to prevent "riding turns" an iron bar called a *norman* was inserted into a hole in the wooden drum between the first two turns of the cable.

The reason these windlass shanties are four-liners and just like hauling ones – as opposed to capstan songs which have a four-line verse and a full chorus – is because the rhythm needed was a jerky one. For instance, in this windlass shanty –

Oh, Stormy's gone *that* good *ol'* man,
Refrain: *To* me way *you* Stormalong!
Oh, Stormy's gone *that* good *ol'* man,
Ay, *ay,* ay – *Mister* Stormalong!

– the syllables in roman show where the men lifted up or pushed down the brakes as they hove in the anchor cable. The first movement, at *Storm,* would (on one brake) be up as far as the waist, at *gone* the arms would be stretched fully above the head, then down to the waist on *good,* down to the feet at *man,* and so on. Of course there were two solos sung by the shantyman and two refrains sung by all hands. Based on the same principle were the *brake pumps,* known to Scandinavian seamen as *nikke-pumpes* or "nodding pumps," the name being very descriptive of the movement entailed. Shanties sung at the brake windlass could be used at brake pumps. Here are two favourites:

She wuz just a village maiden, wid red an' rosy cheeks,
Ch.: *To me way hay hee high ho!*
Oh, she went to church an' Sunday School and sang this anthem sweet,
Ch.: *Oh, there's fi-yer down below!*

I dreamed a dream, the other night,
Ch.: *Lowlands, lowlands away my John,*
I dreamed a dream the other night,
Ch.: *Lowlands away!*

However, in later days, with the use of *Downton pumps* – pumps with huge flywheels – a rotary movement was needed to heave them around and a different type of shanty was

necessary. Any type of song could be sung at the handles and bell-ropes of a Downton pump, and many marches and shore songs were recruited for this chore:

Glory, glory, hallelujah!
Glory, glory, hallelujah!
Glory, glory, hallelujah!
As we go rollin' home.

German sailors sang:

Glori, glori, glori, gloria,
Schön schmeckt der Wein in Batavia!

Dutch mariners yelled out something similar. The *bell-rope* was looped around each pump handle to allow more men to pump ship.

The *capstan* – the double-headed one for anchor work – was the fetish at which the sailor sang his best. By breasting and pushing around the *handspikes,* two or three men at each bar, the great drums of the iron windlass under the fo'c'slehead revolved, heaving the anchor cable inboard. In the earlier operation of heaving the ship to her anchor, fast capstan songs would have been sung, but as the ship neared her anchor and the tempo slackened a slower song such as "Rolling Home" or "Shenandoah" would have been used. An earlier quick shanty would be:

Hurrah! Hurrah! for the gals of Dub-a-lin town,
Hurrah for the bonnie green flag an' the harp widout the crown!

or:

Oh, wake her! Oh, shake her!
Oh, wake dat gal wid de blue dress on,
When Johnny comes down to Hilo – poor ol' man!

Crew at work changing the mainsail of the Macquarie, *a job sometimes accompanied by a sing-out.*

Of other types of shanties we should mention the *bunt-song,* "Paddy Doyle's Boots," used when rolling a sail onto the yard, and the *ceremonial shanty,* "The Dead Horse," both given below in the music section.

The sailor's song of leisure was called the *forebitter,* named from the practice of sailors in fine weather sitting on the *forebitts* – a pair of metal bollards on the fo'c'slehead. Unlike the shanties and capstan songs, which were usually unaccompanied, forebitters would be accompanied by any instrument to hand – squeeze-box, fiddle, banjo, and so on. The songs were mainly of a narrative type, telling of a voyage or a nautical event, but many shore songs, too, particularly drinking songs, were roped in for such leisure-hour singsongs. The usual place and time for fo'c'sle singsongs, complete with fufu band, was in the trade winds during the second dog-watch (6–8 p.m.), or in continental ships, which had no dog-watch, after the evening meal. Whalers, of course, had their own songs; for instance:

'Tis advertised in Boston, New
    York, an' Buffalo,
Five hundred brave Americans a-
    whalin' for to go.

And in the early days of emigration to Australia (1850s) and America (1840s) and during the California goldrush, many songs relating to such passages were sung by seamen, such as this one of the goldrush days:

Oh, I remember well, the lies they
    used to tell,
Of gold so bright it hurt the sight,
An' made the miners yell.

OUTWARD AND HOMEWARD BOUND

Sailing-ship men signed on their ships, depending on place and period, in many ways. In British and continental ports a sailor would wander down to the docks looking for a canvas banner rigged between the shrouds of a ship, signifying she needed hands. A common custom in American ships was that of signing on at the capstan-head. A ship's saloon would sometimes be the temporary office where the men would put a cross to their names agreeing to a three-year contract to sail the seas between latitudes 70°N and 60°S. In the mid-nineteenth century unscrupulous crimps and boarding-house masters set up spurious shipping offices, charging the seamen extortionate fees – what they called "shipping money" but which the seamen referred to as

"blood money" – for the privilege of "signing on." A further extension of such houses was the Shanghai Game (see page 60). A sailor without "papers" or with a "black discharge" from a previous ship could very often join a ship by the time-honored method of the "pier-head jump." If one of the crew had failed to join, or was ill, a final call would come from a ship passing out through the pierheads for a "hand" to appear.

Having arrived aboard his ship – beachcomber, bank-clerk, boot-boy, or a proper sailorman; drunk, sober, or doped according to his method of signing on – the "hand" would amble for'ard and ensconce himself and his sea-chest or bag in a bunk. It was his "castle" for the voyage, unless he was thrown out by some cock-o'-the-fo'c'sle. He'd bring with him his "donkey's break-fast" (straw paillasse) bought from some tailor or ship's chandler, blankets, tin plate and pannikin, shoddy oilskins, seaboots, and Cape Horn gear. Next would come the cry to "Standby, fore 'n' aft!" if the ship were in dock; if in the roadstead it would be "Standby to heave short!" In some ports, if the crew were too drunk to turn to, runners would take the ship out to the Bar, loose and set the sails, and return home by means of the tug. When the capstan was manned, whether by the ship's own crowd or the runners, a shanty would be raised and the collective raucous voices of the heterogeneous crew of true seamen, beachcombers, and adventure-seeking youths would declare to the sea-gulls that the ship was on her way to "furrin parts" – outward bound. "Homeward bound" – these two words were guaranteed to enliven the heart of any sailing-ship man. Mind you, life aboard ship in the days of sail was so tough and full of deprivation that it was rather rare for fo'c'slehands to make a round voyage. This being the case, in British ships – apart from apprentices, the idlers (cooks, stewards, petty officers, and "chips"), and mates – most of the homeward-bounders would be beachcombers (from the West Coast of South America), runaway sailors who'd had enough of the "bush," or fed-up emigrant lads (in Australia and New Zealand). Later we will explain in detail the ritual carried out in the nitrate ports (under the shanty "Goodbye Fare-ye-well") when the loaded ships of Britain, France, and Germany left the Flaming Coast of Chile homeward bound for Europe.

26

SPANISH LADIES

ENGLISH: FOREBITTER, sometimes
used at the Capstan

This is essentially a song of the British
Royal Navy, but it was soon purloined
by merchant seamen and became very
popular with them indeed. It is a narrative song describing the passage of a
sailing naval fleet up the English Channel.

Fare-well an' a-dieu to you fair Span-ish la-dies, Fare-well an' a-dieu to you la-dies of Spain, For we've re-ceived or-ders for to sail for Old Eng-land, An' hope ve-ry short-ly to see you a-gain.

Ch.: We'll rant an' we'll roar, like true British sailors,
We'll rant an' we'll rave across the salt seas,
Till we strike soundings in the Channel of Old England,
From Ushant to Scilly is thirty-four leagues.

2. We hove our ship to, with the wind at sou'west, boys,
We hove our ship to, for to take soundings clear,
In fifty-five fathoms with a fine sandy bottom,
We filled our main tops'l, up Channel did steer.

3. The first land we made was a point called the Deadman,
Next Ramshead off Plymouth, Start, Portland, and Wight,
We sailed then by Beachie, by Fairlee, and Dungyness,
Then bore straight away for the South Foreland Light.

4. Now, the signal was made for the Grand Fleet to anchor
We clewed up our tops'ls, stuck out tacks an' sheets,
We stood by our stoppers, we brailed in our spankers,
And anchored ahead of the noblest of fleets.

5. Let every man here drink up his full bumper,
Let every man here drink up his full bowl,
And let us be jolly and drown melancholy,
Drink a health to each jovial an' true-hearted soul.

The distance between the Ushant and
the Scillies is different in every version
– 34, 35, and 45 leagues (a league
equals three statute miles). Fifty years
ago Nova Scotiamen took this song
and altered it to suit the passage of a
Bluenose ship homeward bound. It has
been said that the master of a homeward-bound sailing ship, unable to get
true observations and in fog for many
wintry days, could recognize the fact
that his ship was in the Channel when
the leadsman and the watch took a cast
with a deep-sea lead, the leadsman
shouting forth loudly, "Fifty-five fathoms an' a fine sandy bottom!" Seamen
have corrupted the names of the headlands – "Deadman" is the Dodman,
"Ramshead" is Rameshead, and "Fairlee" is Fairlead.

RIO GRANDE

ENGLISH/AMERICAN:
CAPSTAN

This song was sung when the men started to heave the anchor and pushed the handspikes before them at a leisurely pace. Why Rio Grande do Sul, in Brazil, was such a magnet to the sailing-ship sailor is hard to say. It was a difficult river (in fact it was a lagoon) to negotiate, being full of shifting sandbanks. The Liverpool "judies" were the tough females of Irish extraction who wore black woollen shawls, voluminous skirts, and elastic-sided Jemima boots.

Oh, a ship went a-sail-ing out o-ver the Bar, 'Wa-ay for Ri-o-o! They've point-ed her bow to the South-ern Star, An' we're bound for the Ri-i-o Grande! Then a-way bul-lies, a-way! 'Wa-ay for Ri-o-o! Sing fa-are-ye-we-ell, me Li-ver-pool gels, An' we're bound for the Ri-i-o Grande.

2. Oh, say wuz ye never down Rio Grande?
   It's there that the river rolls down golden sands.

3. We wuz sick o' the beach when our money wuz gone,
   So we signed in this packet to drive 'er along.

4. There's some of us sick, aye, there's some of us sore,
   We've scoffed all our whack an' we're looking for more.

5. Our anchor we'll weigh an' the rags we will set,
   Them Liverpool Judies we'll never forget.

6. Ye Parkee Lane Judies we'll 'ave ye to know,
   We're bound to the south'ard, Oh, Lord let us go!

7. Oh, pack up yer donkeys an' get under weigh,
   Them Judies we're leaving will git our half-pay.

8. Cheer up, Mary Ellen, an' don't look so glum,
   On white-stockin' day ye'll be drinkin' hot rum.

Sailors' wives were (and still are) allowed a monthly allotment from their husbands' pay. On a specified day of the month they would don their "best bib an' tucker" and haul on their white cotton stockings – trying to be ladies, if only for a day – and then visit the shipping office for their money. Such a day was called "White-Stocking Day." Park Lane was a street in Liverpool much frequented by such women.

SHENANDOAH

AMERICAN: CAPSTAN SHANTY,
used when drawing a ship nearer to her anchor.

The verses of this shanty may be more familiar to the reader in another form, but this is the version which sailing-ship men sang aboard ship throughout the Seven Seas. It probably came into being among the American boatmen of the Ohio, Missouri, and Mississippi rivers sometime in the 1840s. It was also a favorite song among the frontier types – the "Long Knives" (cavalry), mountain men, and backwoodsmen.

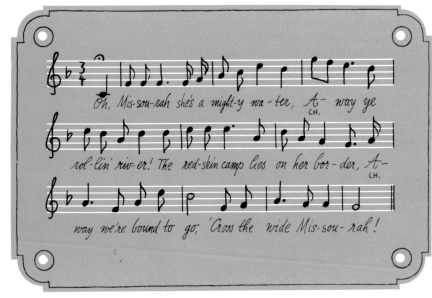

Oh, Mis-sou-rah she's a might-y wa-ter, A-way ye rol-lin' riv-er! The red-skin camp lies on her bor-der, A-way we're bound to go, 'Cross the wide Mis-sou-rah!

2. Oh, Shenandoah was a redskin maiden,
   And a white man loved that redskin maiden.

3. Oh, the white man loved the Indian maiden,
   With trade-goods his canoe was laden.

4. The chief refused the trader's dollars,
   My daughter ye shall never follow.

5. At last there came a Yankee skipper,
   Who winked his eye and tipped his flipper.

6. He sold the chief some firewater,
   And stole the gal across the water.

7. O Shenandoah I love yer daughter,
   I'll take her sailin' 'cross yon rollin' water.

Finally the song came to roost on the wharves and levees of ports in the Gulf of Mexico. Here it was sung at work by the men who loaded bales into the holds of the cotton *droghers*. Deep-water seamen, on hearing the black stevedores singing it, made it their own by "saltwater-fying" it, and spread it across the watery world. The name Shenandoah is probably a corruption of the name of a famous chief of the Oneida Indians, Skenandoah.

VI STYRTE UTÖVER ATLANTEN

SCANDINAVIAN:
HALYARD SHANTY

Callao, Peru, toward which the ship in the song is heading, was well known to whalers and to saltpeter and guano carriers. It had a notorious sailortown, with its pubs and dives – the "Live and Let Live," the "Liverpool Bar," "Smokey Joe's," the "German Bar," and "Neptune." And its crimps and prostitutes were many – Yellow Jake, Jimmy the Pig; Serafina and Madame Gashee (both mentioned in sailor song); Liverpool Annie, who kept the "Liverpool Ship"; and Alec Townsend, the boarding-house master.

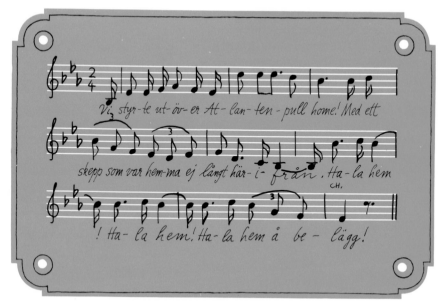

Vi styr-te ut-öv-er At-lan-ten – pull home! Med ett
skepp som var hem-ma ej långt här-i-från. Ha-la hem
! Ha-la hem! Ha-la hem å be-lägg!

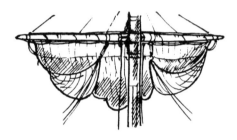

2. *Ho va fin, ho va grann. Var eneste man – pull home! –
Satte segel i topp, och på länsande lopp stack vi ut.*

3. *Calliä var vår hamn, dit vi gå – pull home! –
Som en lus på en tjärad näver, å hå!*

4. *Provianten den tröt, men skepparn skröt – pull home! –
Sa vi dreja till remmen å bäd svalt å frös.*

WE SET OUT OVER THE ATLANTIC

1. We set out over the Atlantic – pull home! –
   With a ship whose home-port was not so far from here.
   Ch.: Haul them home! Haul them home! Haul them home and belay

2. Ho, be fine; ho, be right, every single man – pull home! –
   Set sail to the masthead, and running free we set out.

3. Callao was our port, thence we go – pull home! –
   Like a louse on a tarry fist, O ho ho!

4. The provisions exhausted, the skipper he swore – pull home! –
   We starved and we froze nigh unto death.

SACRAMENTO

AMERICAN/ENGLISH:
CAPSTAN SHANTY

This capstan song came into being aboard the great American fliers – *Sea Witch, Romance of the Seas, Flying Cloud*, and so on – ships which raced around Cape Horn toward the new El Dorado of the Sacramento River, near San Francisco. The California goldrush of 1848–49 brought into being many songs about the men and life of the time.

Oh, a-round Cape Horn we are bound for to go, To me
Hoo-dah, to me Hoo-dah! A-round Cape Horn, thro' the
sleet an' the snow, To me Hoo-dah, Hoo-dah, day!
Blow, boys, blow, for Cal-i-forn-eye-o, There's
plen-ty o' gold, so I've bin told, On the banks of the Sa-cra-men-to!

2. Oh, around the Horn with a main-skys'l set,
   Around Cape Horn an' we're all wringin' wet.

3. Oh, around Cape Horn in the month of May,
   Oh, around Cape Horn is a very long way.

4. Them Dago gals we do adore,
   They all drink vino an' ax for more.

5. Them Spanish gals ain't got no combs,
   They comb their locks with tunny-fish bones.

6. To the Sacramento we're bound away,
   To the Sacramento's a hell o' a way.

7. We're the buckos for to make her go,
   All the way to the Sacramento.

8. We're the buckos for to kick her through,
   Roll down the hill with a hullabaloo.

9. Round the Horn an' up to the Line,
   We're the bullies for to make her shine.

10. Ninety days to Frisco Bay,
    Ninety days is damn good pay.

It is obvious that this shanty is a relative of, if not the same as, Stephen Foster's "Camptown Races." Who composed the first version is a matter of conjecture and argument, but we do know that seamen were singing this song at the capstanhead in the year 1849, whereas Foster did not copyright his song until 1850. As soon as gold was found at Sutter's Creek, Frisco expanded rapidly, becoming a magnet for deserting seamen, Chileno whores, ticket-o'-the-leave men, and miners. Ships were run up on the beach after their passage round the Horn and became silted in. The hulk of the brig *Euphemia* was made into a prison, that of the ship *Apollo* became a saloon, and the *Niantic* was turned into a bunkhouse – the foundation of the well-known Frisco hotel which bears the same name.

PADDY LAY BACK

ENGLISH:
FOREBITTER AND CAPSTAN

This is a fairly old song dating back to the African slaves who toted cotton into the holds of ships in ports along the Gulf of Mexico. But before that it was well known in the packet ships of the Atlantic and is probably of Liverpool origin. Among the packet rats the final chorus was sung "Raise tacks, sheets, an' mains'l haul!" It got its present chorus when it became popular with the seamen aboard the Cape Horn ships engaged in the saltpeter trade of Chile. It faithfully depicts the drunken sailorman waking up aboard a vessel bound for who-knows-where with a ragtail, bobtail crew – some sailormen, some beachcombers – culled from the four corners of hell. Sometimes as many as nineteen or more verses were sung at anchor-heaving.

'Twas a cold an' drear-y morn-in' in De-cem-ber (De-cem-ber), An' all of me mon-ey it wuz spent (it wuz spent), Where it went to, Lord, I can't re-mem-ber (re-mem-ber), So down to the ship-ping-of-fice went (went, went), Pad-dy lay back (Pad-dy lay back)! Take in yer slack (take in yer slack)! Take a turn a-round yer cap-stan, heave a pawl (heave a pawl)! 'Bout ship, sta-tions, boys, be han-dy (be han-dy)! For we're bound for Val-la-pa-rais-er, 'round the Horn!

2. That day there wuz a great demand for sailors
For the Colonies and for Frisco and for France
So I shipped aboard a Limey barque the Hotspur
An' got paralytic drunk on my advance

3. Now, I joined her on a cold December mornin',
A-frappin o'me flippers to keep me warm.
With the south cone a-hoisted as a warnin',
To stand by the comin' o'a storm.

4. I woke up in the mornin' sick an' sore,
An' I knew I wuz outward bound again;
When I heard a voice a-bawlin' at the door,
"Lay aft, men, an' answer to yer names!"

5. 'Twas on the quarterdeck where first I saw 'em,
Such an ugly bunch I'd niver seen afore;
For there wuz a bum an' stiff from every quarter,
An' it made me poor ol' heart feel sick an' sore.

O DU GLADE SJÖMAN

SCANDINAVIAN:
CAPSTAN AND WINDLASS SONG

This song was sung at the capstan of the Swedish ship *Zaritza*, in 1870, when her anchor was heaved up and she worked her way out between the buoys of the London River. This ship was one of Robertsfor's "family-and-farmer" ships.

The ship in this song would be one of the small wooden barks which left the fjords of Norway outward bound with lumber toward the ends of the watery world. The seaman would wave goodbye to his sweetheart or wife silhouetted against the white cottage encircled with green pines. This vignette of a sailing day was one common enough in Scandinavia and the Baltic countries and a lot different from sailing days witnessed in the great ports of Hamburg, Rotterdam, and Antwerp.

O du gla-de sjö-man, nu du lam-nar det-ta land
För att re-sa ik-ring värl-den på den vi-da o-ce-an.

2. *Du är glad och förnöjd och du sjunger med fröjd,*
   Och ditt hopp det står till Herran uti himmelens höjd.

3. *Ankartåget hivas in, seglen brassa foglig vind,*
   A en man tager roret mens de andra klarar opp.

4. *Sen på dacket all man vinkar vi till de på strand,*
   A ett ömt farval vi sander till vårt kära fosterland.

5. *Nu är allting gott å klart, skeppet börjar göra fart,*
   Lilla stugan uppa naset ser oss sakta glida bort.

6. *Där med tåren uppå kind och rätt sorgsen uti sind,*
   Star den mö jag fästat haver, nell, vi ses nog inom kort.

7. *Dagen lider not sitt slut, natten ser förfärlig ut,*
   A det stormar å det viner i varendaste klut.

8. *Solen den har krupit ner, stjärnor synas iche mer,*
   Vredgad bölja jagar fram, söker oss att bryta ner.

9. *Brott och bränningar på hav, skeppet lider därutav,*
   Mangen stolt sjöman där funnit har och bäddat sin grav.

O YE MERRY SEAMEN

1. Now you are leaving this country,
   To sail around the world and 'cross the wide ocean.
   (Repeat all as chorus)

2. Merry and contented, you sing so cheerfully,
   Putting your faith in the Lord and high Heaven.

3. The cable is hove in, the sails are braced tautly.
   A hand to the wheel, and the crowd coil down.

4. Toward the shore fond farewells are sent,
   A tender farewell to our dear homeland.

5. Now we're trim and taut, the ship gathers way,
   The little cottage on the strand sees us sail away.

6. There stands my sweetheart with tear-stained cheeks,
   Sad is she but we'll soon meet again.

7. The day is dying, and the night is growing wild,
   The wind is howling in every stay and sail.

8. The sun has gone – no stars are to be seen,
   The seas are wild – tearing at our sides.

9. The ship is laboring heavily – the water pours aboard,
   Many fine seamen have found a watery grave.

SANTIANA

AMERICAN:
WINDLASS AND CAPSTAN SONG

As were most four-line shanties, this song was first used at the brake-windlass. It is one of fair age and was popular with both whalermen and merchant seamen. It is thought to have originated during the Mexican War, but some authorities believe it may have stemmed from a prayer to the Breton Saint Anne.

Oh, San-ti-an-a gain'd the day, A-way San-ti-an-a! (CH.)
San-ti-an-a gain'd the day, All a-cross the plains of Mex-i-co! (CH.)

Antonio López de Santa Anna, 1794–1876, President of Mexico.

In the Mexican War British seamen favored the Mexican cause, deserting ship to join Santiana's ragtail, bobtail army. Of course the sailor yarn about General Taylor "running away" is historically wrong, since it was General Santa Anna who gave up the city of Monterrey to Taylor. Some versions of this song have nothing whatsoever to do with the war. One version gets mixed up with Captain Stormalong (and his son) and sings of "building a ship of a thousand ton" which the crew load up with "Jamaicy rum." "I'd give ye whiskey and lots of gin, An' stay in the port that we wuz in" is one of its many interesting sentiments.

2. He gained the day at Molley-del-rey,
   An' General Taylor ran away.

3. All of his men were brave an' true,
   Every soldier brave and true.

4. Oh, Santiana fought for fame,
   Oh, Santiana gained a name.

5. An' Zacharias Taylor ran away,
   He ran away at Molley-del-rey.

6. Santiana's men were brave,
   Many found a soldier's grave.

7. 'Twas a fierce an' bitter strife,
   Hand to hand they fought for life.

8. An' Santiana's name is known,
   What a man can do was shown.

9. 'Twas on the field of Molley-del-rey,
   Santiana lost a leg that day.

10. Oh, Santiana fought for his gold,
    What deeds he did have oft been told.

11. Oh, Santiana's day is o'er,
    Santiana will fight no more.

12. Oh, Santiana's gone away,
    Far from the field of Molley-del-rey.

The Washington Irving, built in East Boston, Mass., 1845. From an anonymous watercolor.

The port of Liverpool (right) in the early nineteenth century.

34

LEAVING OF LIVERPOOL

ENGLISH: FOREBITTER

The first version of this fine old fore-bitter to be printed was that sung to W. M. Doerflinger by an aged mariner, Dick Maitland of Sailors' Snug Harbor, New York. Maitland had been shantyman aboard Downeast (Yankee), Bluenose (Nova Scotian), and Limey (English) square-riggers.

I'm bound to California,
By way of ol' Cape Horn,
An' I bet that I will curse the day
An' the hour that I was born.

I've shipped in a Yankee clipper ship,
Davy Crockett is her name.
Captain Burgess he is tough, me lads,
And the mate he's just the same.

'Tis me second passage with ol' Burgess,
An' I think I knows him well.
If a man's a sailor, he can get along,
But if not, he's sure in hell.

Fare-ye-well to Lower Frederick
            Street.
Anson Place, and Parkee Lane,
'Tis a long, long time, me bucko boys,
Ere I see you again.

So, fare-ye-well my own true love,
Goodbye, my love, goodbye.
'Twill be a long, long time, my dear,
But my darlin' don't ye cry.

Liverpool once had two sailortowns – the Southend and the Northend. Ships from the Southend docks took general cargo out to San Francisco and Puget Sound (Washington), returning with cargoes of grain and lumber. Lower Frederick Street is in the Southend and was known as "Flukey Alley." It was inhabited by Puerto Rican, Scandinavian, and Hawaiian seamen. These latter, in many cases, had been sperm-whale harpooners. They got fed up with whaling in the Pacific, joined a Liverpool-bound grain ship, and paying off in Liverpool, stayed there. They gave the nickname "Flukey Alley" to Lower Frederick Street.

GOODBYE FARE-YE-WELL

ENGLISH/AMERICAN:
WINDLASS AND CAPSTAN SONG

This is probably the most popular of all homeward-bound shanties, particularly aboard ships leaving the nitrate ports of the Flaming Coast (Chile). It was well known aboard French and Norwegian ships (see: "As-tu Connu le Pèr' Lanc'lot?").

Oh, don't-ye hear-the Old-Man say?

Good-bye, fare-ye-well! Good-bye, fare-ye-well! Oh,

CH. don't ye hear-the Old-Man say? Hoo-

CH. raw, me boys, we're home-ward bound!

2. We're homeward bound to Liverpool town,
Where all them Judies they will come down.

3. An' when we gets to the Wallasey Gates,
Sally an' Polly for their flash men do wait.

4. An' one to the other ye'll hear them say,
Here comes Johnny with his fourteen months' pay!

5. Them gals there on Lime Street we soon hope to meet,
Soon we'll be rollin' both sides of the street.

6. We'll meet those fly gals an' we'll raise merry hell,
With them flash Judies we'll ring the ol' bell.

7. I'll tell me old mammy when I gets back home,
Them gals there on Lime Street won't leave me alone.

8. We're homeward bound to the gals of the town,
Stamp up me bullies an' heave it around.

9. An' when we gets home, boys, won't we fly around,
We'll heave up the anchor to this bully sound.

10. We're a fine flashy packet an' bound for to go,
With the gals on the towrope we cannot say no!

When a ship deeply loaded with saltpeter was leaving the ports of Caleta Bueno, Taltal, Antofogasta, and Mejillones, among others, the men from other ships in the line would board the homeward-bounder in order to swell the chorus of this shanty. The seamen would be of many nationalities but the English chorus was known to them all. The previous evening a wooden crucifix bearing four lanterns, symbolizing the constellation of the Southern Cross, would have been hoisted to the yardarm. This, bell-ringing, and wild "hurrahs!" from all the ships in port would be part of the ritual of "Godspeeding the homeward-bounder."

OUTWARD AND HOMEWARD BOUND

ENGLISH:
FOREBITTER AND CAPSTAN SONG

This song was originally either a naval or East Indiaman's song – Malabar being a port better known to fighting ships or ships of the Honorable John Company. The purser serving out the grog (i.e., rum and water) was more of a naval than a merchant-ship custom. Rum, unlike what the writers of nautical fiction would have us believe, was only served out in English merchant-men after a storm or a particularly difficult task.

The word "grog," as used in the British Navy, comes from the custom of a certain Admiral Vernon, in the eighteenth century, wearing a deck-cape of grogram – a tough waterproof materi-

To the Liv-er-pool docks we'll bid a-dieu, To Sal an' Kate an' Bes-sie, too, The an-chor's a-weigh, an' our sails are un-furl'd, An' we're bound to plow the wat-ry world, Hur-rah, we're out-ward bound, Hur-rah, we're out-ward bound!
CH.

al. Because of this he was known as "Old Grog"; and as he was the first naval officer to water his crew's rum, the rum got the nickname "grog." Both American and British seamen sang this song but each would give his own particular port – "To Pensacola town…," "To the Catherine docks…." But the docks from which the ship sailed in the original song were the Milbay docks of Plymouth, England.

2. Oh, the wind blows hard from the east nor'east,
The ship will sail ten knots at least;
The purser will our wants supply,
An' while we've grog we'll never say die.

3. An' if we touch at Malabar,
Or any other port as far,
The purser then will tip the chink,
An' just like fishes we will drink.

4. An' when our three years they are out,
'Tis jolly near time we went about,
An' when we are home and once more free,
Oh, won't we have a jolly spree.

5. An' when we gets to the Liverpool docks,
The pretty gals come down in flocks,
One to the other ye can hear them say,
Here comes Johnny with his three years' pay.

6. An' then we'll haul to the Bull an' the Bell,
Where good liquor they do sell.
In comes the landlord with a smile,
Sayin', "Drink up, lads, while it's worth yer while."

7. But when the money's all spent an' gone,
None to be borrowed, none to be lent,
In comes the landlord with a frown,
Sayin', "Get up, Jack, let John sit down!"

8. Then poor ol' Jack must understand,
There's ships in port all wanting hands,
He goes on board as he did before,
An' he bids adieu to his native shore.

ADIEU MADRAS

FRENCH: FOREBITTER

This song is said to come from the period (1830–48) when Louis-Philippe ruled France. I believe it to be at least a hundred years older, from the time when France ruled a large part of India. That was before the Carnatic district (with Madras and Pondicherry) was captured by the English and an Indian prince, favorable to English interests, was put in charge. A native girl tries to delay the sailing of her *matlow* (seaman) but is too late to gain the necessary permit. The life of luxury it suggests by way of silk clothes, neckerchiefs, and so on, is usually associated with gentlemen, and not sailors, east of Suez.

A-dieu Ma-dras, a-dieu fou-lards, A-dieu rob' soie, a-dieu col-lier, choux, Dou-dou à moin, li ka pa-ti, Hé-las, hé-las, cé pou tou-jou, Dou-dou à moin, li ka pa-ti, Hé-las, hé-las, cé pou tou-jou!

2. *Bonjou Monsieur le Gouverneur,*
   Moin vini faire une pétition,
   Pou mandé ou autorisation,
   Afin laissé doudou ici.

3. *Non! non! non! non! dejà trop tard,*
   Batiment a dejà sur la bouée,
   Non! non! non! non! dejà trop tard,
   Dans un instant, appareiller.

4. *Adieu Madras, adieu foulards!*
   Adieu grains d'or, adieu colliers, choux!
   Doudou à moin, li ka pati,
   Hélas, hélas, cé pou toujou!

GOODBYE MADRAS

1. Farewell Madras, farewell neckerchiefs,
   Goodbye silk clothes, goodbye collar, darling.
   Sweetheart of mine – li ka pati,
   Alas, alas, it is for ever!
   (Repeat last two lines in each verse)

2. Good day – Governor!
   I've come to make a petition,
   For you to give me authorization,
   So as to keep my sweetheart here.

3. No! no! no! no! It is too late,
   The ship is ready at the buoy,
   No! no! no! no! It is too late,
   At this very moment she's ready to sail.

4. Farewell Madras, farewell neckerchiefs,
   Goodbye beads of gold, goodbye collars, darling,
   Sweetheart of mine – li ka pati,
   Alas, alas, it is for ever!

ROLLING HOME

ENGLISH:
CAPSTAN SONG AND FOREBITTER

When sung as a forebitter two of the shanty verses are made into one. As "Goodbye Fare-ye-well" was the accepted homeward-bound song of the Chilean coast, "Rolling Home" was usually sung aboard ships leaving Australia.

The original of this song is said to have been written as a poem by Charles Mackay aboard ship; on the other hand it is possible Mackay based his poem on the singing of the sailors. This version is more nautical than the usual one with less of Mackay's couplets. American seamen often sang the shanty changing "dear Old England" to "dear New England." German seamen were also partial to it, sometimes singing the English-worded chorus to German verses and sometimes, though less often, using the following chorus:

Segler Heim, Segler Heim,
Segler Heim wohl übers Meer,
Segler Heim zur Deutschen Heimat,
Segler Heim mein Lieb zu dir.

Call all hands to man the cap-stan, See the ca-ble flaked down clear, Heave a-way, an' with a will, boys, For Ol' Eng-land we will steer. Rol-lin' home, rol-lin' home, Rol-lin' home a-cross the sea, Rol-lin' home to dear Ol' England, Rol-lin' home, fair land, to thee.

2. Now Australia, we are leavin',
   For Old England give a cheer,
   Fare-ye-well, ye dark-eyed damsels,
   Give three cheers for English beer.

3. Goodbye, Heads, we're bound to leave you,
   Haul the towrope all in-board.
   We will leave Old Aussie starnwards,
   Clap all sail we can afford.

4. Round Cape Horn on a winter's mornin',
   Now among the ice an' snow,
   Ye will hear our shellbacks singin'
   Sheet her home, boys, let her go!

5. Eighteen months away from England,
   Only fifty days, no more,
   On salt horse and cracker-hash, boys,
   Boston beans that make us sore.

6. Now the Lizard Light's a-shinin',
   An' we're bound up to the Nore,
   With the canvas full an' drawin',
   Soon we'll be on England's shore.

LEAVE HER, JOHNNY, LEAVE HER

ENGLISH/AMERICAN:
CAPSTAN AND PUMP

This was what was known as the "Paying-off Shanty," since it was used either to warp a ship through the lock-gates by means of the capstans or to man the pumps for the last time before the crew was paid off. When on the high seas, any refusal of duty or back-talk, however slight, would be punished in a draconian manner. There was, however, an unwritten law that a sailor could sing about his feelings, be they ever so rebellious. And this was the song that was often used.

Oh, the times wuz hard, an' the wa-ges low,
Leave her, John-ny, leave her! But now once more a-shore we'll go, An' its time for us to leave her!
Leave her, John-ny, leave her, O-oh, leave her, John-ny, leave her! For the voy'ge is done, an' the winds don't blo-ow, An' it's time for us to leave her!

2. Oh, I thought I heard the Ol' Man say,
Tomorrow ye will get your pay.

3. The work wuz hard an' the voyage wuz long,
The sea wuz high an' the gales wuz strong.

4. The wind wuz foul an' the sea ran high,
She shipped it green an' none went by.

5. The grub wuz bad an' the wages low,
But now once more ashore we'll go.

6. Oh, our Ol' Man he don't set no sail,
We'd be better off in a nice clean jail.

7. We'd be better off in a nice clean jail,
With all night in an' plenty of ale.

8. She's poverty-stricken an' parish-rigged,
The bloomin' crowd is fever-stricked.

9. Oh, sing that we boys will never be
In a hungry bitch the likes o' she.

10. The mate wuz a bucko an' the Old Man a Turk,
The bosun wuz a beggar with the middle name of work.

11. The Ol' Man swears an' the mate swears too,
The crew all swear, an' so would you.

12. It's growl yer may, an' go yer must,
It matters not whether yer last or fust.

13. The ship won't steer, nor stay, nor wear,
An' so us shellbacks learnt to swear.

14. We'll leave her tight an' we'll leave her trim,
An' we'll heave the hungry bastard in.

40

SAILORS, THEIR WORK, GROUSES AND DEMISE

There is a vague conception in the minds of many landlubbers that the captain takes the wheel to drive the ship and stays in that position the whole voyage! The truth, of course, is that in the days of sail the captain had all the responsibility of being in charge of an isolated microcosm, but with no physical duties himself. He was the chief navigator (and often the only one), the overseer of the weather, the sails, the officers and men, and everything to do with the progress of the ship. In the days of sail there used to be a rather crude saw, modified here, in which a description of the powers of a captain ran thus: He can give you birth, baptize you, marry you, try you, hang you, have intercourse with you, but he can't put you in the family way! He led a lonely life, rarely speaking to any other than the chief mate, and unless he had a hobby was often a secret drinker.

Some ships were happy ships, the masters mixing with the men in deck sports, but this was rare. There was a bigger gulf between the offi-

cers and men than even that between the masters and the officers. This was the pattern mainly in deepwater ships; in coasting vessels, such as those in the Baltic, there was more of a "family" atmosphere. From the moment seamen joined a deepwater ship they were "kept at it." Apart from the normal routine jobs of wheel and lookout, and the handling of the sails and cordage, a ship was "like a lady's watch – always in need of repair." Hence, daily, there were jobs such as "sailorizing" – like splicing and turning in dead-eyes, helping the sailmaker, doing running repairs high in the rigging, cleaning the brasswork and the "bright-work," and holystoning the decks. Naturally the sailor groused and growled to let off steam, muttering such time-worn lines as "Who'd sell a farm an' go to sea?" and "When I pay off this packet I'll march inland with an oar over me shoulder. When someone queries 'What's that yer carrying?' I'll drop me anchor an' there I'll stay" – a line direct from the *Odyssey!* – and "The man who goes to sea for fun would go to hell for a pastime." But still they returned to this life time and time again. In their few leisure hours they would sing, play instruments, dance, put ships in bottles, make models and mats, and scrape scrimshaw designs on whales' teeth. From the vicissitudes of such a life they often gained rheumatism, ruptures, and death by falling from aloft or drowning. Dying at sea, with little comfort around them and the captain the only doctor, they were quickly dropped over the side. A sailor version of the burial service at sea runs:

For *man that is born of woman, has but a short time to live,* He *goes up like a fore topm'st stays'l, comes down like a flyin' jib.*

That's your seaman – a humorist to the end!

STRIKE THE BELL

ENGLISH: PUMPING SHANTY

The tune of this pumping song is well known throughout the world of folksong. "Ring the Bell, Watchman" is a Scottish song bearing this air, and the Welsh song "Twll Bach y Clo" also uses this tune, while in Australia, in the sheep-shearing sheds, there is a number called "Click Go the Shears." Which song can claim to be the original is difficult to say, but I would venture that this sailorsong is one of the oldest.

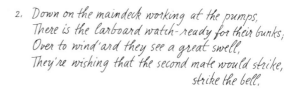

2. Down on the maindeck working at the pumps,
There is the larboard watch-ready for their bunks;
Over to wind'ard they see a great swell,
They're wishing that the second mate would strike,
strike the bell.

3. Aft at the wheel poor Anderson stands,
Grasping the spokes in his cold mitten'd hands,
Looking at the compass an' the course is clear as hell,
He's wishing that the second mate would strike,
strike the bell.

4. For'ard on the fo'c'slehead keeping sharp lookout,
There is Johnny standing, ready for to shout,
"Lights burnin' bright, sir, an' everything is well!"
He's wishin' that the second mate would strike,
strike the bell.

5. Aft on the quarterdeck our gallant captain stands,
Lookin' to wind'ard with his glasses in his hand,
What he is thinkin' of, we know very well,
He's thinking more of shortening sail, than strike,
strike the bell.

Aft on the poop—deck, walk-in' a-bout,

There is the se-cond mate, so stead-y an' so stout.

What he is think-in' of, he on-ly knows him-sel', O, we

wish that he would hur-ry up an' strike, strike the bell.

Strike th' bell, se-cond mate, let us go be-low,

Look well to wind-ard, ye can see it's gonna blow,

Look at the glass, ye will see it has fell, An' we

wish that ye would hur-ry up an' strike, strike the bell!

On shipboard time has always been kept by the striking of the ship's bell, and a twenty-four-hour day would be divided into so many "watches," something known even in biblical times. In English and American ships the length of the watch was four hours, with the exception of the first (4–6 p.m.) and the last (6–8 p.m.) dogwatches, which were of two hours each to allow the seamen to have different hours of work every alternate day. In German and Scandinavian ships a long afternoon watch was common – noon to 6.30 p.m., then the watch would go below until midnight. From midnight they stood the watch until 4 a.m., below from 4–8 a.m., and on deck again until midday, then they would have the long afternoon below. In French ships one watch went below at 8 p.m., came on deck at midnight until 4 a.m., went below until 7.30 a.m., then kept the deck until 9 a.m. and went below again until 11.30 a.m. These hours were arranged to agree with continental mealtimes. In ancient times on Anglo-Saxon ships the *grommet* or deckboy would turn the half-hour sandglass at midday (eight bells). When all the sand had run out, he would strike the bells. He did this every half hour – one bell for 12.30, two bells for 1 p.m., and so on until the end of the four-hour watch when eight bells were rung. Aboard German ships to this day *ein Glass* to *acht Glass* is used for the watch half-hours, still keeping alive the reference to the half-hour sandglass.

AS-TU CONNU LE PÈR' LANC'LOT?

FRENCH: HALYARD SHANTY

This is obviously a French version of the English capstan song "Goodbye Fare-ye-well," but Jean Matelot used it for hauling instead of heaving. It was very popular with the hardy seamen of the French *cachalot* (sperm) whalers who scoured the South Pacific in search of their giant prey. These whalers made their headquarters at Nuku Hiva, in the Marquesas, the island where Herman Melville was a beachcomber after deserting a Yankee whaler.

It is interesting to note that during the American War of Independence (1775) many of the New England whaling ports were blockaded and fired on by British men-o'-war. Also at sea British naval vessels preyed on the Yankee whalers, until most of the whaling

As-tu con-nu le Pèr'Lanc'lot? Good-bye fa-re well, good bye fa-re-well! Qui fait la pêche aux cach-a-lots, Hour-ra! Oh Mex-i- co-o-o-o!

2. Il a trois filles qui font la peau,
   Il a trois filles qui font la peau.

3. L'une à Lorient, l'autre à Bordeaux,
   La troisième est à Colombo.

4. Il donne la goutte à ses mat'lots,
   A coups de barre et de guindeau.

5. Il mange la viande, nous laiss' les os,
   Il boit du vin et toi de l'eau.

6. A la manoeuvre le bosco
   Te dresse à coups de cabillot.

DID YOU KNOW OLD FATHER LANCELOT?

1. Did ye know old Father Lancelot?
   Ch.: Goodbye, farewell, goodbye, farewell!
   He who fishes for big *cachalot*.
   Ch.: Hurrah! Oh Mexico!

2. He has three daughters – trollops all,
   He has three daughters – on the game.

3. One in Lorient, another in Bordeaux,
   The third she lives in Colombo.

4. He gives us sailors gout, me boys,
   With his handling of the helm and windlass.

5. He eats meat – for us the bones,
   He drinks wine, but water for you.

6. When we're working ship, the old hunchback,
   Drills us with a belayin'-pin across the back.

fleets were depleted. This caused many of the New England whaling families, from New Bedford and Nantucket, to ask to be transported – lock, stock, and barrel – to the Welsh port of Milford Haven and to the French port of Dunkerque.

LES TROIS MARINS DE GROIX

FRENCH: FOREBITTER

The incident given in this song – the footrope of a yard parting and a sailor falling into the sea – was not an uncommon happening in the days of sail. In late-nineteenth-century sailing ships the footropes were of wire and were often brought down from aloft, stretched by means of the capstan, and thus tested for weaknesses. In the earlier ships, however, they were of hemp and naturally more liable to break if not constantly attended to. If the falling sailor fell overboard (in the daytime) there was always the possibility of picking him up, but if he hit the deck his chances were nil. Sometimes the bellying of a sail would cushion his fall and then he would be lucky.

Nous é-tions trois ma-rins de Groix, Nous é-tions trois ma-rins de Groix,– Em-bar-qués sur le Saint Fran-çois, Montra-dé-ri, tra, la, la, la, Mon tra-dé-ri, tra, la, lai- ré!

THE THREE SAILORS OF GROIX

2. Embarqués sur le Saint François,
   Gagnant quarante-cinq francs par mois.

3. Gagnant quarante-cinq francs par mois,
   Et du vin à tous les repas.

4. L'captaine donne un coup d'sifflet,
   "Pare à serrer les perroquets."

5. "Pare à serrer les perroquets!"
   Le marchepied z-il a cassé.

6. Le marchepied z-il a cassé,
   Le matelot tomba z-à l'eau.

7. Le matelot tomba z-à l'eau,
   Et l'on met la chaloupe à l'eau.

8. Et l'on met la chaloupe à l'eau,
   On n'retrouva que son chapeau.

9. On n'retrouva que son chapeau,
   Son garde-pipe et son couteau.

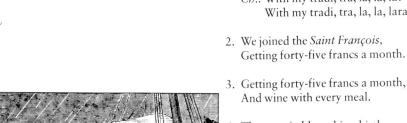

1. We are three sailors of Groix,
   (Repeat first line in each verse)
   We've joined the Saint François.
   Ch.: With my tradi, tra, la, la, la!
        With my tradi, tra, la, la, laray!

2. We joined the Saint François,
   Getting forty-five francs a month.

3. Getting forty-five francs a month,
   And wine with every meal.

4. The captain blows his whistle,
   "Stand by to clew up the t'gallants'l."

5. "Stand by to clew up the t'gallants'l,"
   The footrope has parted.

6. The footrope has parted,
   A sailor falls into the sea.

7. A sailor falls into the sea,
   And the shallop is lowered.

8. The shallop is lowered,
   But they only find his hat.

9. They only find his hat,
   His pipe-guard, and his knife.

RETOUR DU MARIN

FRENCH: FOREBITTER

This seasong comes from the days of Louis XIII (1610–43) when France was engaged in wars with Spain and, later, Holland. The story of the French *matelot* in this song is one that has been reduplicated many times throughout the world – Jean Matelot, Jan Maat, or Jack Tar comes home from a long voyage or the wars to find his sweetheart has married another or his wife, thinking him dead, has remarried. The classic tale of this kind is the poem by Tennyson – *Enoch Arden*.

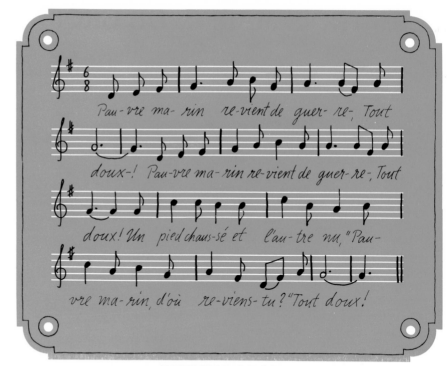

Pau-vre ma-rin re-vient de guer-re, Tout doux–! Pau-vre ma-rin re-vient de guer-re, Tout doux! Un pied chaus-sé et l'au-tre nu, "Pau-vre ma-rin, d'où re-viens-tu?" Tout doux!

RETURN OF THE SAILOR

2. "Madame je reviens de guerre, Tout doux!
   Qu'on apporte ici du vin blanc,
   Que le marin boive en passant!" Tout doux!

3. Brave marin se mit à boire, Tout doux!
   Se mit à boire et à chanter,
   Et la belle hôtesse à pleurer, Tout doux!

4. "Qu'avez-vous donc la belle hôtesse, Tout doux!
   Regrettez-vous votre vin blanc,
   Que le marin boit en passant?" Tout doux!

5. "C'est pas mon vin que je regrette, Tout doux!
   C'est la perte de mon mari,
   Monsieur, vous ressemblez à lui." Tout doux!

6. "Ah! Dites-moi, la belle hôtesse, Tout doux!
   Vous avez de lui deux enfants,
   Vous en avez quatre à présent." Tout doux!

7. "Quant j'ai reçu de ses nouvelles, Tout doux!
   Il était mort et enterré,
   Et je me suis remariée." Tout doux!

8. Brave marin vida son verre, Tout doux!
   Sans remercier, tout en pleurant,
   Et regagna son bâtiment. Tout doux!

1. Poor sailor coming back from the wars – All is fine!
   (Repeat first line in each verse)
   One foot shod, the other nude,
   "Poor sailor, from whence come ye?" – All is fine!

2. "Madame, I have come home from the wars – All is fine!
   Bring me some white wine
   That I may drink a while" – All is fine!

3. The gallant sailor drinks the wine – All is fine!
   He drank and he sang,
   But the lovely hostess cried – All is fine!

4. "What is the matter with you, lovely hostess – All is fine!
   Are you sorry for your white wine
   That the sailor is drinking" – All is fine!

5. "It is not my wine that I regret – All is fine!
   It's because I've lost my husband,
   Mister, he looked like you" – All is fine!

6. "Ah, tell me, my lovely hostess – All is fine!
   Didn't you have two children by him –
   And now you have four" – All is fine!

7. "When they wrote and told me the news – All is fine!
   That he was dead and buried,
   I married again" – All is fine!

8. The gallant sailor drank his wine – All is fine!
   Without thanks and sorrowful,
   Went back to his ship – All is fine!

EJ BÖR VI SÖRJA, EJ BÖR VI KLAGA

SCANDINAVIAN: HALYARDS

The wind-pump mentioned in this song was to be seen in all of the small sailing barks of Norway at the end of the last century. The "Baltic barks" were built of wood and, to use a sailor expression "leaked like a basket." Sailors, on joining such a ship, would lift a hatch and smell the odors coming up from the hold. If the hold stank to high heaven, the sailor would be satisfied; if it smelled sweet, he knew that the ship was leaking and he would head ashore. The windmill pump saved many hours of the heart-breaking work known in ships having only manual pumps.

Ej bör vi sör-ja, ej bör vi kla-ga, Kon-sta-peln, vår vän, han är all-tid oss när,

Han har oss lo-vat att hand om oss ta-ga,

Trots al-la mots-park, vart vind-en än bär,

Han har oss lo-vat att hand om oss ta-ga,

Trots al-la mots-park, vart vind-en än bär.

WE MUST NOT GRIEVE, WE MUST NOT GROUSE

1. Oh, we must not grieve, we must not grouse,
   The steward, our friend, is always near us,
   For he has promised in hand to take us,
   What so wind may blow, however we may cuss.
   (Repeat last two lines in each verse)

2. Oh, we must not grieve, we must not grouse,
   The wind-pump we have is as the tread-mill light,
   Murmur'd grumbles you will rue,
                    for the steward will catch you,
   And now to reef the sail, for she's pumped dry.

3. Oh, we must not grieve, we must not grouse,
   The steward has weighed out our bread, pork,
                    and herring,
   If this skipper's pleased, he'll let the rope-end fall,
   We'll get extra victualling, every single night.

2   Ej bör vi sörja, ej bör vi klaga,
    Den vindpump vi har går som trampvarnen lätt,
    Om det gnisslar i pipen, knstapeln begriper'n,
    Och revar dess segel, för nu slår hon läns.

3. Ej bör vi sörja, ej bör vi klaga,
    Konstapeln han vager upp sill, brö å flask,
    Om skepparn belåten, han lirkar på tåten,
    Vi får extra förplägning var eviga kväll.

CANTU À TIMÙNI

SICILIAN/ITALIAN: FOREBITTER

This steersman's song comes from Trapani, a once-famous port for American and other deep-water sailing ships in the salt trade to Western Sicily. It is still a fishing port of importance.

The Sicilian word for helmsman – *timùni* – is one that gave rise to various names for a tiller, helm, and helmsman. In Italian it is *timoniere*. The original Italian word *timone* describes the beam of a plow, the pole of a carriage, or the horses harnessed to the pole as opposed to the leading horses. In France a *timonier* was a ship's helmsman and in eighteenth-century England the man at the wheel was referred to as a "timoneer." Later, in English ships, a sort of tell-tale informing the officer of the watch the position of the helm was called a "timon-o'-guy"; and the word "timenoguy" was used for any piece of rope or lanyard without a proper name, even in recent times.

2. Er a lu Munti li picciotti beddi,
'N Trapani deci'rana su'un carrinu,
'N Trapani deci'rana su'un carrinu,
A lu Munti se'picciuli un granu.

3. La Missa e la rici lu parrinu,
E chiddu chi la servi sacristanu.
Lu zuccu vivi acqua e nesci vinu.
L'occhi juncino prestu di luntanu.

This is a song of the helmsman on the high seas. As he passes the headlands of Western Sicily he muses about the ports along the coast. It is sung in Sicilian dialect, contains proverbs, and is difficult to translate, but it would appear to be:

SONG OF THE HELMSMAN

1. Sciacca is noted for its fish-spears [skewers],
Mazzara for the salting of fine herring,
At Marsala they catch fish by the dozen,
And Trapani is known for its pink coral.

2. At Munti the girls are beautiful,
In Trapani ten beads make a rosary [necklace],
At Munti six small ones [boys] make a rosary bead.

3. The Mass [La Missa] is said by the priest,
Helped, in the Sacraments, by the sexton.
The vine drinks water and produces wine.
Eyes quickly reach the distance.

HALARVISA

SCANDINAVIAN: HAULING SONG

This song was given by its informant "Navigation Pelle" as a hauling song, though it has some characteristics of a capstan shanty. In Captain Sternvall's fine collection of sea songs, *Sång Under Segel* of 1935, it is said to have originated in 1875.

Although a rather jolly song, musically its refrains are much the type of thing the Scandinavian sailor used when "singing-out" on a rope. Scandinavians, incidentally, were good at this form of keeping time when hauling hand-over-hand, on a piece of cordage. The common "sing-outs" of such seamen were:

Kärre, värre, vitt bom-bom!,
Nicke, dicke, dickum, plutt!,

and

Fantali, fantali viktoria-oria!

Tailors, apparently, were much the same in Swedish ports as their counterparts were elsewhere, demanding extortionate prices for the shabby gear they sold impoverished seamen – leaky seaboots and oilskins, cheap underwear, and poor quality jerseys.

2. *Vem älskar ej en ung sjöman!*
   Han rusar jämt i faran fram.

3. *Såväl i mödan som i strid,*
   I flickans famn han vilar sig.

4. *En skräddare är en daglig gäst,*
   Han fordrar mig för byx och väst.

HAULING SONG

1. A sailor sails so far away,
   Ch.: Cherry-very-vit bom-bom!
   When he comes home the girls are gay,
   Ch.: Cherry-very-vit bom! Hurrah so!
   Full Ch.: Victoria! Victoria!
   Cherry-very-vit bom! Hurrah so!
   Victoria! Victoria!
   Cherry-very-vit bom-bom!

2. Who does not love a sailor dear?
   He is a man who knows no fear.

3. At work or fighting Jack's the chap,
   At love he also knows his job.

4. The tailor is his daily guest,
   Demanding payment for his vest.

BEN BACKSTAY

ENGLISH: FOREBITTER

In the eighteenth century Charles Dibdin portrayed in his songs the life of a naval seaman as one of romance and patriotism, hardly mentioning the ubiquitous pressgang. Since his songs induced young farmers, students, bank clerks, and others to volunteer for the Navy, the Lords of the Admiralty gave him a pension. The song we give here was not composed by Dibdin but is couched in his style and is one of the few so-called nautical ballads, produced ashore by literary types, that the sailor took as one of his own.

2. One day our gallant captain,
   A very jolly dog,
   Served out unto the whole ship's crew,
   A double whack of grog.

3. Which made Ben Backstay tipsy,
   All to his heart's content,
   An' while he was half-seas over,
   Right overboard he went.

4. A shark appeared on the starboard side,
   An' sharks no man can stand,
   For they just gobble up everything,
   Just like them sharks on land.

5. They threw him out some tuckling,
   Of saving him they'd hopes,
   But since the shark bit off his head,
   He could not see the rope.

6. And now his headless ghost appeared,
   All on the briny lake,
   An' calling all the hands right aft,
   Said, "By me a warning take."

7. "Through drinkin' grog I lost my life,
   An' lest my fate ye meet,
   Don't ever mix your rum me boys,
   But always take it neat."

WHERE AM I TO GO, ME JOHNNIES?

AMERICAN/ENGLISH:
HALYARD SHANTY

This hauling song comes from the West Indies. It was collected from a wonderful black shantyman called by the singular title of Harding the Barbadian Barbarian.

Where am I to go me John-nies? O, where am I to go? To me way, hay, hay, high, roll an' go! O, where am I to go me John-nies? O, where am I to go? For I'm a young sail-or boy, an' where am I to go?

In the days of sail part of the making of a ship's boy into an able-bodied seaman, or A.B., consisted of training him in the art of going aloft and stowing a sail. The highest sails – the royals and t'gallants (in German and Scandinavian ships, *royals* and *bramsegels;* in French ships, the *coquetois* (cockatoos) and *perroquets*) – were the boys' special concern. They had to loose them when the order came and stow them in a blow. After racing aloft they would edge out side-ways, crablike, along the two-inch footropes and pummel the sail until they had subdued it and could secure them with ties called gaskets. When the job was done satisfactorily, they would slide down the backstays to the deck.

2. 'Way up on that t'gallant yard, that's where yer bound to go,
   'Way up on that t'gallant yard, the gans'l for to stow.

3. 'Way up on that t'gallant yard and take that gans'l in,
   'Way up aloft an' lay right out an' stow it neat an' trim.

4. Yer bound away around Cape Horn that's where yer bound to go,
   Yer bound away around Cape Horn, all through the ice an' snow.

5. Ye'll be an able seaman, lad, when you have served yer time,
   An' then ye'll ship as a sailorman aboard the Blackball line.

6. One day ye'll sit for a ticket, lad, this work will serve ye fine,
   Ye'll finish up as a captain, lad, aboard some liner prime.

7. Oh, where am I to go, me Johnnies, where am I to go?
   Oh, where am I to go, me Johnnies, where am I to go?

METTONS LA CHALOUPE À L'EAU

FRENCH: FOREBITTER

This was a rather popular fo'c'sle song with the French merchant seamen of the 1840s and 50s. The theme of this song – that of an old sailor spinning a yarn – was a rather common one in the ballads of sailors. The technical name of the lifeboat dropped from the davits of the ship in the song – *chaloupe* – is one which was used for small boats throughout the world.

Met-tons la cha-loupe à l'eau, Met-tons la cha-loupe à l'eau, Mat-e-lot tom-ba dans l'eau, M'en-ten-dez-vous? Et si toi, te fous de moi, Moi, je me fous de vous.

Whether the English word for a small boat – shallop, shalloop – came from the French (as did many merchant-ship words) or vice versa, it is difficult to say, but in the English Middle Ages small light fishing vessels with a fore and main mast, each carrying a lugsail, were called "shallops," "shalloops," or even "sloops." Small shallops were used as tenders to English men-o'-war, and in the French Navy a *chaloupe* was often a small gunboat, carrying one heavy gun and a crew of forty. On the other hand, a shallop can be a small boat rowed by one or two men, and as such was known in the days of the *Mayflower* and the early Quakers on the New England coast of America.

2. *Matelot cassa sa bras,*
   Chirurgie il était là…

3. *Lui voulut qu'on lui coupa,*
   Matelot ne voulut pas…

4. *Vers le port il s'en alla,*
   Et c'est là qu'il achète…

5. *Une pipe et du tabac,*
   Et mon histoir' finit là…

GET THE BOAT IN THE WATER

1. Get the boat in the water,
   (Repeat first line in each verse)
   A sailor has fallen overboard…
   Ch.: Do you understand me?
   And if you think I'm talking rubbish,
   Well, I feel the same about you.

2. The sailor's arm was broken,
   And the surgeon he was there…

3. Was he willing to be amputated,
   The sailor was not willing…

4. When the ship reaches port,
   There you will buy me…

5. A pipe and tobacco,
   Now my yarn is ended…

54

THE SAILOR'S GRAVE

ENGLISH: FOREBITTER

The original of this song was composed in 1859 by Eliza Cook (lyrics) and John C. Baker (tune). Down through the years it has suffered at the hands of seamen by what is known as the "folk process," with the results that in its present form it has come a long way from the original.

Our bark was far, far from the land, When the bra-vest of our gal-lant band, Went dead-ly pale, an' pined a-way, Like the twi-light of an au-tumn day.

Burial at sea – the result of ship fever, malnutrition, dysentery, scurvy, falling from aloft, or being killed by gear falling from aloft in battle (once known as "yellow fever") – was always a dismal affair and would upset a ship's company for days. In the latter-day, undermanned sailing ships of all nations it also meant extra work for those left behind. In the English Navy of years ago, the sailmaker would sew up the corpse in his hammock, then one of the officers would put the last stitch through the septum of the nose, precluding resuscitation when in the water (in the manner of the Comte de Monte Cristo in Dumas' famous story) and thus preventing desertion by this means. In the merchant service the custom was to put the final stitch through the lobe of the left ear, in the belief that this was nearer to the heart of the dead man and would show a reflex action if he were still alive.

2. We watched him through long hours of pain,
Our hopes were great, our task in vain,
His end was near, we felt sad qualms,
But he smiled and died in his shipmates' arms.

3. He had no costly winding sheet,
We placed two round shot at his feet,
And we sewed him up, he was canvas-bound,
Like a king he lay in his hammock sound.

4. We proudly decked his broken chest,
With the "Blood 'n' Guts" * across his breast,
The flag we gave as a mark o' the brave,
And he was ready for a sailor's grave.

5 Our voices broke, our hearts were weak,
And wet was seen on the toughest cheek,
We lowered him down o'er the ship's dark side,
And he was received by the rollin' tide.

6. With a splash and a plunge and our task was o'er,
And the billows rolled as they rolled before,
And many a wild prayer hallowed the wave,
As he sank deep to a sailor's grave.

*Sailor name for the Red Ensign of Britain

55

BOLD MAC CARTENEY

ENGLISH: FOREBITTER

This was a favorite song of the Western Ocean packet rats – those tough Irish sailormen who manned the forerunners of the Cunard and other Atlantic steamship lines. The Blackball, Swallowtail, Red Cross, Black Diamond, and other lines of sailing packet ships not only had tough masters and mates but their crews were all, to use an old-time sailor expression, "hard men to shave." These ships were the first in the world to run a monthly schedule of sailings.

Come all ye bold sea-far-in' men, an' list-en to me tale, Con-cer-nin' bold Mac-Cart-en-ey, in Li-ver-pool town did dwell, Down by the Salt-house docks one day, as he did chance for to stray, On board a west-bound pack-et ship, he stow'd himself a- way.

2. As down the Mersey we set sail, to New York we wuz bound,
This poor young lad began to think of the friends he'd left behind,
This poor young lad began to think of his friends and his native shore,
And he cursed the day he'd stowed away on the City of Baltimore.

3. When he came out of his hiding place, the mate to him did say,
"What made ye stow aboard this ship; come tell to me, I pray,
Among these wild Irish packet rats, you'll have wished you'd
                                        have stayed ashore,
An' ye'll curse the day ye sailed away on the City of Baltimore."

4. 'Twas early every mornin' the mate he turned us to,
'Twas early every mornin' he tried to kick us through,
"Where is that Irish stowaway?" the mate, I heard him say,
"I'm here," sez Bold MacCarteney, "What do yer want of me?"

5. Now the mate he being a cowardly dog, for MacCarteney did go,
An' with an iron belayin' pin he tried to lay him low,
But MacCarteney being a smart young chap as he'd often
                                        proved ashore,
He laid the mate upon his back in the City of Baltimore.

6. The second mate and bosun came to the mate's relief,
But with a heavy ol' capstan bar he made 'em both retreat,
His Irish blood wuz boilin' now, an' then we heard him roar,
"Oh, skin and hair will fly this day on the City of Baltimore."

7. The cap'n, a Nova Scotiaman, MacDonnel wuz his name,
An' when he heard the fight, me buckos, right for'ard then he came,
Sez he, "Me bold MacCarteney, you're a regular son-o'-a-whore,
I'll make ye bosun of my ship, the City of Baltimore."

Aboard such packet ships there existed an unwritten rule known as the "Western Ocean Law." Fisticuffs have always dominated fo'c'sle life, and in most ships if a sailor could "floor" the presiding "cock-o-the-walk," he would then take this position in the fo'c'sle. In the packet ships, however, advancement by way of the fist was even greater. If one could lay out the bosun, one could become the bosun. Without a large amount of nautical knowledge, and certainly without any navigational acumen, a common able seaman could work himself up in stages, by way of his "dukes," to be chief mate, if he was a better man at handling himself than were the officers. Iron discipline certainly *was* needed in these ships, and physical prowess came before nautical know-how. In this song, our hero – a landlubber – manages to become bosun of the good ship *City of Baltimore* thanks to his fisticuffs.

It is thought that the named ship was a sail-carrying steamer of the Inman line of Liverpool.

PORTS, HARLOTS, SHANGHAIING AND PRESSGANGS

Sailor John, Jan Maat, Jean Matelot, Johann Teer, or Skangast knew the streets of the ports of the world like the back of his hand. When convivial in a pub with shipmates he would rattle them off as though he were a tourist with a Baedeker in his hand: Antwerp's Schipperstraat, Rotterdam's Schiedamschedijk, Cardiff's Oriental Parade, London's Ratcliffe Highway, Marseilles' Vieux Port, New York's South Street, Hongkong's Ship Street, Hamburg's Sankt Pauli, and the Boca of Buenos Aires. Home to the sailor, in many cases, was where he hung his hat. He would bandy about the names of pubs like confetti – the "Last Chance" in Antwerp, "Annie Cunningham's" in Liverpool, the "Blue Post" in London, the "Irish Consul" in Marseilles, the "Fore Royal Bar" in Pensacola, the "Bells of Shandon" in

Frisco and the "German Bar" in Callao – and when it came to name-dropping, the names of fancy women dropped from his tongue in a stream – Liverpool Lizzie of Portland, Mother Brady and Bremer Mary of the Chile Coast, Nellie Norman of Newcastle, N.S.W., Pigeon-toed Sal of Frisco, Grosse Louise and Marie Con Vache of Bordeaux, and Mimi San of Yokohama.

During the last century and the early days of the present one, shanghaiing was the favorite game in the sailortowns of the world. The word probably came into use after the 1848 goldrush when crews for ships crossing to China were difficult to get, men preferring to join vessels bound for New York or Europe. There had always been some form of trepanning or kidnapping of seamen, usually under the name of "crimping," but it wasn't until this new verb "to shanghai" came into use that the crimps set up a supply and demand system. As soon as a ship appeared off the port, the boarding-house runners boarded the ship, proffering rotgut whiskey to the crowd, helping them to stow the canvas as well as their sea-bags, and taking them ashore in boats before the ship was tied up. Once they had them in their clutches they would sell them back, very often to the same ship, for a high price. This supply and demand system soon spread throughout the ports of the world.

As with the original crimping, pressganging harkens back to the days of the first Queen Elizabeth. In spite of the romantic notion that every boy in Britain is sea-minded,

the fact is that without crimping and pressganging the ships of the navy and merchant service would not have been able to proceed to sea. As naval seamen became too rare in Britain, the government inaugurated the Quota Act, in which all mayors and local councillors had to supply a certain quota of men from their towns and villages, even if it meant emptying their jails.

These men were known at sea as "Newgate Birds" or "King's Hard Bargains." They were a diseased and louse-bound lot but they were the sort of manpower with which Britain staved off the threatened invasion of her islands by, at different times, the Spaniards, the Dutch (called "Hogan-mogans" by the seamen), and the French (known as "Johnny Crapeau").

CURAÇAO

DUTCH: FOREBITTER

Curaçao, nowadays the great oil port of the Dutch Antilles, was in the old days, along with Aruba, a well-known port-o'-call for Dutch West Indiamen. Limestone was an early cargo which drew other countries' ships as well to those isolated islands. Welsh schooners sailed there so often that it was said there was a white trail across the Atlantic, known to seamen as "The Milky Way." This white track was caused by the milky limestone water pumped out from the bilges of such ships. Dutch sailors have known for years the ladies of easy virtue of the once infamous street called Heren Straatje, in the port of Willemstad, Curaçao. The sailor in this song has come to know the crafty wiles of the local prostitutes, but then again he prefers their temporary and doubtful company to life on shipboard with the harrassing mates bawling unceasingly

in his ears. However, by the last verse – when the ship is loaded and ready to leave – he knows he's homeward bound and will soon be in the arms of his wife, whose embraces he praises when compared to the murky charms of the shady ladies of Curaçao.

2. 'k Kwam laarst, met hanst, al door 't Herenstraatje,
   Men sprak: "Mijn lieve maatje, kom zet u hier wat neer,
   En drink met ons een glaasje, en rook een pijp tabak,"
   Dan met al die loze streken raakt 't geld uit de zak.

3. Een zoen, kandoen, de hele nacht te blyven,
   Dan hoort men niet 't kyven van onze officier,
   Zo raken wij aan't dwalen, zo dronken als een zwyn,
   Het schip ligt voor de palen, aan boord moeten we zyn.

4. Maak los, de tros, de voor-en-achter touwen,
   En wilt 't maar aanschouwen, we gaan naar Holland toe,
   Waar is't beter leveb, dan bij een achte vrouw,
   'k Verzeg er al de vrouwtjes voor van't eland van Curaçao.

5. Maak los, de tros, de voor-en-achter touwen,
   Wij zyn niet meer te houwen, we gaan naar Holland toe,
   Waar is beter leven, dan bij je eigen vrouw,
   Vervloekt zijn al de hoeren van't eiland Curaçao.

1. Curaçao, I've seen you so many times,
   And all your crafty tricks, I dislike them,
   And all your crafty tricks, I dislike them,
   Therefore I'm going to depart to where I came from.

2. Last night I went, with haste, all through Lord's Street,
   They said: "My dear sailor, come sit down here a while,
   And drink a glass with us and smoke a pipe of tobacco."
   But with all their crafty tricks, your money goes from your pocket.

3. A kiss can make you stay the whole night long,
   Then you don't hear the bawling of your officer,
   Thus we go roaming, as drunk as pigs,
   The ship lays at the moorings, aboard her we have to be.

4. Loose the hawser, the fore and aft lines,
   And if you wish to see us, we go back to Holland,
   Where life is better with a real woman,
   I give you, therefore, all the little girls of the land of Curaçao.

5. Loose the hawser, the fore and aft lines,
   We're not to be held fast anymore, we go to Holland,
   Where life is better with your own wife,
   Damn all the whores of Curaçao.

LIVERPOOL JUDIES

ENGLISH/AMERICAN:
FOREBITTER often used at the Capstan

This version of a popular Liverpool forebitter sings of the Western Ocean trade and of being shanghaied. Another version is based on a homeward passage from Frisco to the Bramley-moor Dock, Liverpool, by way of Cape Horn. New York, where our hero is talked ashore by a crimp, was a common jumping-off place for seamen disillusioned with the cold winter crossing of the Atlantic from Liverpool to New York or Boston. Many of the

When I--war a youngster I sail'd with the rest, On a Liv-er-pool pack-et bound out to the West, We an-chor'd one day in the har-bor of Cork Then put out to sea for the port of New York. Sing-in CH. roll, roll, bul-lies roll, Them Liv-er-pool Ju-dies have got us in tow.

2. For forty-two days we wuz hungry an' sore,
   Oh, the winds were agin us, the gales they did roar,
   Off Battery Point we did anchor at last,
   Wid our jibboom hove in an' the canvas all fast.

3. De boardin'-house masters wuz off in a trice,
   A-shoutin' an' promisin' all that wuz nice,
   An' one fat ol' crimp he got cotton'd to me,
   Sez he, "Yer a fool, lad, ter follow the sea."

4. Sez he, "There's a job as is waitin' for you,
   Wid lashin's o' liquor an' beggar-all to do."
   Sez he, "What d'yer say, lad, will you jump her too?"
   Sez I, "Ye ol' barstard, I'm damned if I do."

5. But de best o' intentions dey niver gits far,
   After forty-two days at the door of a bar,
   I tossed off me liquor an' what d'yer think?
   Why the lousy ol' barstard had drugs in me drink.

6. The next I remembers I woke in de morn,
   On a three-skys'l yarder bound south round Cape Horn,
   Wid an ol' suit of oilskins an' two pair of sox,
   An' a bloomin' great head an' a dose of the pox.

7. Now all ye young sailors take a warnin' from me,
   Keep a watch on yer drinks whin de liquor is free,
   An' pay no attention to runner or whore,
   Or yer head'll be thick an' yer throat'll be sore.

packet rats manning such ships were poorly clad and half-starved, and as soon as Sandy Hook was sighted, they made up their minds to jump ship.

Of course, as in the song, the promise of a good job ashore rarely came to anything. Around South Street, Cherry Street, and Fulton Street, New York, lived many crimps and boarding-house masters and mistresses. Gallus Meg was a woman chief-bouncer of an establishment called "The Hole in the Wall," owned by One-armed Monell. After a roughhouse with a drunken sailorman, she would bite off his ear and put it, as a trophy, in a pickle jar, beside many others on a shelf behind the bar.

DE RUNER VON HAMBORG

PLATTDEUTSCH: HALYARDS

This is a Plattdeutsch (dialect spoken on the north coast of Germany) version of "Roll the Cotton Down" and was known to every Jan Maat of the old sailing days, when Segelschiffhafen, Hamburg, was chock-a-block with masts and yards. I myself have heard it raised many times aboard a Bremen Cape-Horner. The runners of Hamburg were a notorious lot. A runner was usually a man who took a ship out of port while the crew was sobering up. In Hamburg the term covered boarding-house runners and ships' tailors. *Sneider* is the Plattdeutsch word for tailor (German *Schneider*).

De see geiht hoch, de wind de blast,
CH. Kohm un Beer for mi! Jan-Maat, de fleit, is-
nie ver-baast, Oh, kohm un Beer for mi!
CH.

Such men would meet incoming ships, armed with kümmel and schnapps, offering the homeward-bounder a "sub" of money, prior to being "paid off." When outward bound they would offer these chaps cheap "togs" and during their stay in port supply them with booze and women. They claimed the seaman's advance-note to pay them for this trouble. There were few cases of shanghaiing in Hamburg, but there were numerous sailor pubs, all bearing English names – "Falmouth for Orders," "Channel for Orders," "Liverpool Bar," the "Homeward Bound" – as well as many German *Tanz*-halls and *Bier*-halls, such as the "Cosmopolitan," "El Dorado," "International," "Metropolitan," and the "Hippodrome."

2. Reise aus Quartier un all'an Deck,
De Ool de fiert de Marssails weg.

3. Un wenn wi nu na Hamborg kaamt,
Denn süüt man all' de Sneiders staan.

4. Elias röppt, dor büst du ja,
Ik see di nich tom eersten Mal.

5. Du bruukst gewiss een'neen Hoot,
Ik heff weck von neeste Mood.

6. Un ok gewiss een Taschendook,
Un'n neen Slips, den bruukst du ok.

7. Un ook een beeten Seep un Tweern,
Un denn one pound to'n Amuseern.

8. Wat is dat een lütjen Kööm,
Un een Zigarr, dat smeckt doch schöön.

9. Afmustert ward, dat is mol klor,
Wie gaat von Bord un schreet Hurroh.

THE RUNNERS OF HAMBURG

1. The sea ran, and the wind it blows,
   Ch.: Kümmel and beer for me!
   Sailor John is a rorty chap,
   Ch.: Oh, kümmel and beer for me!

2. Rouse out all hands – away on deck,
   The Old Man wants the tops'ls stowed.

3. And when we now to Hamburg come,
   Ye'll see there all the runners stand.

4. Oh, there you are, Elias, you rogue,
   I've seen you many times before.

5. Well, I know you need a brand new hat,
   I have one in the latest style.

6. And a handkerchief most certainly,
   And a new tie, too, you also need.

7. And also a bit of cotton and soap,
   And one pound for amusement.

8. Oh, what about a drop of kümmel?
   An' a big cigar tasting so fine?

9. I'm paying off, oh, that is clear,
   We'll go ashore and shout hurrah!

HAMBORG DU SCHÖNE STADT

GERMAN: FOREBITTER,
also used for Hauling and Capstan

This seamen's leisure and work song is not one of the normal Plattdeutsch pieces, nevertheless it was a very popular ditty with the Hamburg *Matrosen* (sailors).

The incident in which the sailor gets beaten up and left in the gutter by the prostitute's "heavies" was common, of course, in all the ports of the world. In the song it probably happened in one of the dives of the Reeperbahn in Hamburg.

2. Ich fasst'sie sanft beim Arm,
   Sie aber schaut'mich an,
   "Glauben Sie, ich wär' so eine?"
   Mädchen sie sich schleunigst auf die Beine.

3. Doch ich war sehr galant,
   Drückt ihr Taler in die Hand,
   Die kleine süsse Maus,
   Führt mich dann vor ihr Haus.

4. "Bleib'nur ein Weilchen steh'n,
   Darfst mit aufs Zimmer geh'n."
   Ich stand zwei volle Stund',
   War steif wie'n Pudelhund.

5. Ich sprang voll Wut ins Haus,
   Flog aber gleich heraus,
   Kamen vier Männer in der Nacht,
   Schleppten mich auf die Wach!

6. Schlief dort in guter Ruh',
   Zahlt zweiundzwanzig Schilling dazu
   So kann dir in Hamburg gehn,
   Willst du zum Mädchen gehn.

7. Hamburg, du schöne Stadt,
   Dich hab'ich gründlich satt,
   Zwei Taler zweiundzwanzig Schilling
   bin ich los,
   Und wegen dem Mädel bloss.

HAMBURG, YOU LOVELY TOWN

1. Hamburg, you lovely town,
   Ch.: Oh, my dear, my dear!
   Hamburg, you lovely town,
   Ch.: Oh, my dear, my dear
   'Twas there I met a lovely girl,
   Who put my heart into a whirl.
   Ch.: Oh, 'tis a shame.

2. I took her gently by the arm,
   She looked at me but not with charm,
   "D'ye think I'm that kind o' girl?"
   And off she went in a whirl.

3. But I then turned on the charm,
   And pressed two dollars in her palm,
   And then the little sugar-mouse,
   Led me to the front of her house.

4. "Wait you here, I'll return quite soon,
   While I go up to my room."
   For two full hours I waited there,
   My bones as stiff as an old dead mare.

5. Boiling with rage I climbed the stair,
   But I wasn't long in there,
   Four men came and me they beat,
   And bundled me out into the street.

6. Unconscious there in the street I lay,
   They took twenty shillings — all my pay,
   Thus the sluts of Hamburg score,
   Still we return and ask for more.

7. Hamburg you lovely town,
   You and your girls have done me down,
   Two dollars, twenty shillings short,
   All on account of a girl of this port.

A-ROVIN'

ENGLISH:
CAPSTAN AND PUMPING SONG

Certain authorities, in the past, have
claimed this shanty to be of Eliza-
bethan origin, but I disagree entirely.
The verses describing the progress of
the seduction have a faint resemblance
to those in a song in Thomas Hey-
wood's *Rape of Lucrece* (1640), but
this is a common technique in folksong
and no measure of age.

Other authorities claim that this song
cannot be about the port of Amsterdam, since, if it has the age suggested,
Amsterdam was closed to English
shipping at that time. They think it
may be connected with one or the
other of two seamen's taverns, both
called "The Amsterdam," one on the
riverfront at Gravesend, the other in
St-Georges-in-the-East, London. This
theory too bears little water. Sung in its
entirety by old windbag men this song
was very obscene. Verses which we
have omitted here describe in salacious
detail the various parts of the girl-
friend's body, and the sexual act is
given in nautical terminology.
In later versions, the sailor is depicted
as having signed away in a saltpeter
ship bound for Chile around Cape
Horn, describing how, homeward,
with a full cargo of this stuff, all food,
tobacco, and even socks were filled
with the noxious saltpeter.

2. I met this fair maid after dark,
   She took me to her favorite park.

3. I put me arm around her waist,
   Sez she, "Young man, yer in great haste!"

4. I put me hand upon her knee,
   Sez she, "Young man, yer rather free!"

5. I put me hand upon her thigh,
   Sez she, "Young man, yer rather high!"

6. We laid down on a grassy patch,
   An' I felt such a ruddy ass,

7. In three weeks' time I wuz badly bent,
   Then off to sea I sadly went.

8. Now when I got back home from sea,
   A soger [whaler] had her on his knee.

66

ANE MADAM

NORWEGIAN: HALYARDS

This tops'l halyard shanty was the most popular hauling song raised by Norse seamen aboard Norwegian, Swedish, and Danish sailing ships. Actually it is a form of the English "Blow the Man Down." None of the Scandinavian seaports had regular sailortowns like those found in the ports of France, Germany, Holland, Belgium, and Britain. But even so, there did exist rather tatty streets in the areas near the docks of larger seaports or near the quays of smaller ports. It was there that madams and prostitutes were to be found.

A-ne Ma-dam var en vak-ker smaa-tøs,
Aa- haa! A-ne Ma-dam! A-ne Ma-dam hadd'-en
un-ge paa løs, Aa- haa! A-ne Ma-dam!

2. Kom sjømand tag nu dit hvite seil!
   Kom heis nu dit bramseil ogsaa din røil.

3. Men først en tur i Sandvigen,
   For der at hilse farvel paa pigen.

4. Til Madam Felle undervels stak vi ind,
   For dersteds at opfriske litt vores sind.

5. Men madammen stængte døren med
   stikker og straa,
   At ingen sjømander der skulde gaa.

6. Men saa sprang der op en nordvestlig vind,
   Saa doren sprang op og sjømanden fren ind.

ANNIE MADAM

1. Annie Madam was a beautiful maid,
   Ch.: Ah haa! Annie Madam!
   Annie Madam had a fatherless babe.
   Ch.: Ah haa! Annie Madam!

2. Come seamen now set yer snowy white sails,
   Come hoist yer gans'ls and lofty roy-als.

3. But first let us head out to Sandvigen town,
   An' there with the girls we will let sorrow drown.

4. To Madam Felle's, oh, a visit we'll pay,
   An' from our thick heads clear the cobwebs away.

5. With nettles and straw she had bunged up the door,
   As she'd had her fill of us sailors before.

6. But just then there came a wild nor'west wind,
   The door it burst open – the sailors rolled in.

Ane Madam and Madam Felle would have been such "ladies." Unfortunately, we know very little about them. The translator was of the opinion that the last two verses of this shanty contained double meanings, both rather obscene.

MAGGIE MAY

ENGLISH: FOREBITTER

In earlier versions of this forebitter the
heroine bears the name of Nelly Ray.
The first written mention of this song
is said to be in a diary belonging to
Charles Picknell. He was an able seaman aboard the convict ship, the
Kains, which sailed from London for
the penal settlements of Van Diemen's
Land on 8 July 1830.

Canning Place and Park Lane are both
in the south end of Liverpool and once
part of its infamous sailortown. In
Canning Place, by the statue of Mr.
Huskisson (the first man to be killed by
a railway engine), the black-shawled
Liverpool harlots gathered in quanti-
ties. They were like harpies awaiting
their prey – the homeward-bound,
recently paid-off, deep-water sailor.
Modern versions of this song give Lime
Street, Liverpool, as the location of
Maggie's "parade."

2. I paid off at the Home, after a voyage from Sierra Leone,
   Two pounds ten a month had been my pay;
   As I jingled in my tin, I was sadly taken in
   By a lady of the name of Maggie May.

3. When I ran into her I hadn't got a care,
   I was cruisin' up an'down ol' Canning Place.
   She was dressed in a gown so fine, like a frigate of the line,
   An' I being a sailorman gave chase.

4. She gave a saucy nod, an' I like a farmer's clod,
   Let here take me line abreast in tow;
   And under all plain sail, we ran before the gale,
   And to the Crow's Nest tavern we did go.

5. When I got full of beer, to her lodgings we did steer,
   She charged me fifteen shillings for the fight.
   I was so ruddy drunk when I landed in her bunk,
   I never knew what happened in the night.

6. Next mornin' when I woke, I found that I wuz broke,
   I hadn't got a penny to me name.
   So I had to pop me suit, me John L's, an' me boots,
   Down in the pawn shop, number nine, Park Lane.

7. Oh, you robbin' Maggie May, you robbed me of my pay,
   When I slept wid you last night ashore.
   Guilty the jury found her, for the robbin' of a homeward-bounder,
   An' she'll never cruise down Park Lane any more.

8. She wuz chained and sent away from Liverpool next day,
   The lads they cheered as she rolled down the Bay;
   And every sailor lad he only was too glad,
   They'd sent the ol' whore out to Botany Bay.

WAT WI DOHT

PLATTDEUTSCH:
GANGSPILL or CAPSTAN SONG

This is another type of Sankt Pauli (Hamburg) sailorsong – a sort of catalog of the *deerns* (prostitutes) of David Street and the Groote Freiheit who greeted Jan Maat home from Chile and elsewhere. According to the song there were two categories of Sankt Pauli girls – those who worked from indoor and those, apparently much cheaper, who were the streetwalkers found on the corner of David Street and who charged only "fivepence."

2. *Un ok de lüttje Mary, dat is ne fixe Deern,*
   Kriegst du de mol det Obends faat, denn kannst
   di nich besweern.

3. *Un ok de dicke Anna, dat is ne feine Popp,*
   Kummt Janmaat von lang' Reis' torück, denn passt se
   em glieks op.

4. *Denn gaat wi no Sankt Pauli rop, dor geit dat lustig her,*
   Wenn se di seet, denn schreet se all: Du, Fitje,
   kumm mol her!

5. *Un op de Groote Freiheit, wat is di dor en Karm,*
   Eer du di dat verseen deist, hest glieks ne Deern
   in'n Arm.

6. *Un wenn de Huur verjuchheit is, denn weet ik wat ik do,*
   Ji köönt mi alltosom mol fix, ik go no See hento.

The seamen who sang such a song were the crews who manned the great four- and five-masted nitrate traders of Laiesz, Vinnen, Miller, and other companies, which were engaged in the Cape Horn trade of the latter part of the nineteenth century. The greatest ship in this trade was the five-masted *Preussen*. It was wrecked on the cliffs of Dover in 1910, after being rammed by a steamer.

WHAT WE'LL DO

1. And when we now to Hamburg come,
   Then we know what we'll do,
   We'll buy a gal for fivepence,
   On the corner of David Street.
   Ch.: Hurrah! Hurrah! Hurrah, hurrah, hurrah!
   We'll buy a gal for fivepence on the corner
   David Street.

2. There's also little Mary,
   A smasher of a gal,
   If you catch her in the evening,
   There's no room for complaint.

3. And then there is Fat Annie,
   She is a lovely doll,
   When Johnny he comes in from sea,
   She's waiting for to hook him.

4. Then we go up to St. Pauli,
   There's always something on,
   When they see you they start cheering,
   "Hey, Fritzy – come along!"

5. And up the Grosse Freiheit,
   Oh, lads, what an awful row,
   An' before you know what's happening,
   A girl's hooked on your arm.

6. An' when we have blown all our pay,
   Then I'll know what I will do,
   All you girls can kiss my stern,
   An' I'll go back to sea!

CAN'T YE DANCE THE POLKA?

AMERICAN/ENGLISH: CAPSTAN SONG

This shanty probably had its origin around the 1840s, when the dance called the polka came out of Bohemia to sweep across Europe to America. In its original form the song is rather bawdy, as are most of these sailor ditties which tell of the sailor coming ashore and "catching" (very easily) a so-called flash packet. New York's sailortown was from South Street to Broadway and all the area in between.

The girls there, as the girls of ports elsewhere, were a rather tricky lot — full of dodges whereby their sailor companions could be bilked. On the other hand, some of these girls had a rough existence. On the corner of Broadway and First Street stood a notorious concert-cum-drinking hall patronized by sailors on a drunken cruise around the town. The corner was known as "Suicides Corner." It appears that the prostitutes who frequented this saloon had formed a suicide club, the members of which drew lots as to when each should commit suicide and quit the so-called gay life. Streetwalkers were known as "cruiser girls" and were to be seen on every sidewalk along Bleecker Street, Cherry Street, Chatham Square, Water Street, Fulton Street, South Street, and around Five Points, Hell's Half Acre, and the Bloody Fourth Ward in the 1840s, 50s, and 60s.

The Yankee "bloodboat" our hero joins, probably from some tough boarding house, was perhaps the *Bloody Gatherer,* the *Tam-o-shanter,* the *Commodore T. H. Allen,* or the *Sunrise,* with a bucko (bully) master like Bucko Crocker, Watts, Bully Martin, or Ol' Mose Doyle.

As I walked down the Broad-way, one eve-nin' in Jul-y, I met a maid who ax'd me trade, an' a Sail-or John, sez I—. Then a-

CH.

way you San-tee, My dear An-nie, Oh, ye New York girls, Can't ye dance the pol-ka?

2. To Tiffany's I took her; I did not mind expense,
   I bought her two gold earrings, an' they cost me fifteen cents.

3. Sez she, "You Limejuice sailor, now see me home you may."
   But when we reached her cottage door, she unto me did say,

4. "My flash man he's a Yankee, wid his hair cut short behind,
   He wears a pair of long seaboots, an' he's bosun in the Blackball line."

5. "He's homeward bound this evenin', an' wid me he will stay.
   So git a move on, sailor-boy, git crackin' on yer way."

6. So I kissed her hard an' proper, afore her flash man came.
   An' fare-ye-well, me Bowery gal, I know yer little game.

7. I wrapped me glad rags round me, an' to the docks did steer.
   I'll never court another maid; I'll stick to rum an' beer.

8. I joined a Yankee bloodboat, an' sailed away next morn.
   Don't ever fool around wid gals, yer safer off Cape Horn!

GO TO SEA NO MORE

AMERICAN/ENGLISH: FOREBITTER

When this old forebitter was sung as an anchor shanty at the capstan-head the following chorus would be used:

No more, no more, we'll go to sea no more,
A man must be blind for to make up his mind,
To go to sea once more!

Because of its theme it was a favorite among Pacific whalers. In the song, the sailor is shipped aboard one of the Arctic Right or Bowhead whalers which worked from Frisco up to the Bering Straits. Shanghai Brown, one of the most notorious of Frisco crimps, does not shanghai him in the usual way – doped with laudanum in his beer – but ships him aboard stone-cold sober, all official and correct.

Life in such ships was hell. Sometimes, after passing through the Bering Straits heading for Point Barrow and the Beaufort Sea, they would be caught in the ice and would find it impossible to return. This happened in 1871 when thirty-two out of a fleet of forty whalers became trapped in the ice off Northern Alaska. Beyond belief, everyone escaped by hauling their slim whaleboats over the ice until they reached the open sea and the safety of the other eight ships which had heeded the ice warnings of the Eskimos. Many captains had their wives and children with them on this terrible voyage.

When first I lan-ded in Fris---co-, I went up-on the spree, Me hard-earned cash-, I spent- it fast, got drunk as drunk could be, An' when me mon---ey was- all gone, 'twas then I want-ed more, But a man must be blind for to make up his mind, for to go-- to sea once more.

2. That night I slept wid Angeline, too drunk to roll in bed,
   Me clothes wuz new an' me money wuz too, next morn wid them she'd fled,
   An' as I rolled a-down the street the whores they all did roar,
   There goes Jack Ratcliffe, poor sailor-boy, who must go to sea once more.

3. Now as I wuz rollin' down the street I met ol' Shanghai Brown,
   I axed him for to take me in, he looked at me wid a frown,
   Sez he: "Last time yiz was paid off wid me ye chalked no score,
   But I'll take yer advance an' I'll give ye a chance an' I'll send ye to sea once more."

4. He shipped me aboard of a whaling ship bound for the Arctic Seas,
   Where the cold winds blow, an' there's ice an' there's snow, an' Jamaicky rum do freeze,
   I can't stay here, I have no gear, I've spent all me money ashore,
   'Twas then that I said that I wished I wuz dead so I'd go to sea no more.

5. Sometimes we caught them Bowheads, boys, some days we did catch none,
   Wid a twenty-foot oar stuck in yer paws, we pulled the whole day long,
   An' when the night it came along an' ye dozed upon yer oar,
   Yer back so weak, yiz never could seek a berth at sea no more.

6. Come all ye bold seafarin' men and listen to me song,
   When yiz come off of them damn long trips I'll tell yiz what goes wrong,
   Take my advice, don't drink strong drink, nor go sleepin' wid any ol' whore,
   But get married lads, an' have all night in, an' go to sea no more!

RATCLIFFE HIGHWAY

ENGLISH: FOREBITTER

In the early part of the last century, Ratcliffe Highway, London, and its environs was the greatest center of vice, with the most infamous of all sailortowns throughout the world. Ratcliffe Highway, and its adjacent Wellclose Square – known to seamen as "Tiger Bay" – developed its reputation with the growth of the London Docks. Even today some of its side streets bear nautical names, such as the North East Passage and Ship Alley.

As I wuz a-roll-in' down the High-way one morn, I spied a flash pack-et from ol' Wap-ping town; As soon as I seed her I slacked me main brace, An' I hoist-ed me stun-'sls an' to her gave chase. Oh, me rig-gin's slack, Aye me ratt-lin's are fray'd, I've ratt-led me rig-gin' down Rat-cliffe High-way!

Wilton's Music Hall, dating from these days, has been preserved by the London council. It has a special gallery for sailors and their girls. Other famous pubs and dance halls of those days were the "Prussian Eagle" in Ship Alley; the "Hole-in-the-wall"; the "Old Mahogany Bar," where the clipper-ship seamen would foregather; and "Paddy's Goose," actually the "White Swan," whose landlord became famous during the Crimean War by enlisting men on his premises to go and fight the Russians. This song is full of double-entendres, which partially hides its bawdy story. The word "lazareet" is a corruption of lazaretto, a hospital treating contagious diseases.

2. I fired me bow-chaser, the signal she knew,
She backed her main tops'l an' for me hove to;
I lowered down me jolly-boat an' rowed alongside,
An' I found madam's gangway wuz open an' wide.

3. I entered her little cubby-hole, an' swore, "Damn yer eyes!"
She wuz nothin' but a fireship rigged up in disguise;
She had a foul bottom, from sternpost to fore,
'Tween the wind and the water she ran me ashore.

4. She set fire to me riggin', as well as me hull,
An' away to the lazareet I had to scull;
Wid me helm hard-a-starboard as I rolled along,
Me shipmates cried, "Hey, Jack, yer mainyard is sprung!"

5. Here's a health to the gal wid the black, curly locks;
Here's a health to the gal who ran me on the rocks;
Here's a health to the quack, boys, who eased me from pain.
If I meet that flash packet I'll board her again.

JEAN FRANÇOIS DE NANTES

FRENCH: HALYARD SHANTY

This French shanty is a close relative of the English one, "Boney Was a Warrior"; the *Oh, mes boués!* (Oh, me boys!) phrase and the word *oué* (way), are obviously of English origin. The name "François" was pronounced by French seamen as "Fransway."

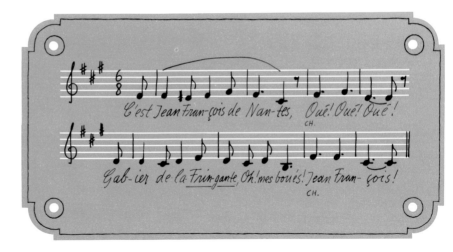

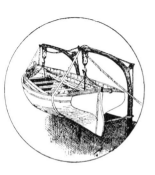

2. Débarqu'en fin d'campagne,
   Fier comm'un roi d'Espagne, Oh! mes boués!

3. En vrac dedans sa bourse,
   Il a vingt mois de course, Oh! mes boués!

4. Une montre', une chaîne,
   Valant une baleine! Oh! mes boués!

5. Branl' bas chez son hôtesse,
   Bitte et boss et largesse, Oh! mes boués!

6. La plus belle servante,
   L'emmèn dans sa soupente, Oh! mes boués!

7. De conserve avec elle,
   Navigue sur mer belle, Oh! mes boués!

8. Et vidant la bouteille,
   Tout son or appareille, Oh! mes boués!

9. Montr' et chaîne s'envolent,
   Mais il prend la vérole, Oh! mes boués!

10. A l'hôpital de Nantes,
    Jean François se lamente, Oh! mes boués!

11. Et les draps de sa couche,
    Déchire avec sa bouche! Oh! mes boués!

12. Pauv' Jean François de Nantes,
    Gabier de la Fringante! Oh! mes boués!

JEAN FRANÇOIS OF NANTES

1. Oh, Jean François of Nantes,
   Ch.: Way! Way! Way!
   Topman of the *Frisky*, Oh! me boys!
   Ch.: Jean François!

2. He comes ashore after his voyage,
   He's as proud as the king o' Spain, Oh! me boys!

3. Loose gold has he in his purse,
   Twenty months' wages lying there, Oh! me boys!

4. He also has a chain and watch,
   Fit to be worn by a whale, Oh! me boys!

5. Commotion at his landlady's,
   Bollard an' painter an' bounty, Oh! me boys!

6. The maid most beautiful of all,
   Carries him up off to her loft, Oh! me boys!

7. And together with this gal,
   Sails he on a sunlit sea, Oh! me boys!

8. And emptying his big bottle,
   All his gold it sails away, Oh! me boys!

9. Watch and chain soon gone-o,
   An' he gets a "curio," Oh! me boys!

10. In a hospital in Nantes port,
    Jean he there bemoans his fate, Oh! me boys!

11. The sheets and cases of his bed,
    With his teeth he tears to shreds, Oh! me boys!

12. Poor Jean François of Nantes,
    Topman of the *Frisky!* Oh! me boys!

BLOW THE MAN DOWN

AMERICAN/ENGLISH:
HALYARD SHANTY

This was the number one hauling song of the Western Ocean packet rats – most versions being associated with Liverpool, although there does exist a Ratcliffe Highway version. Paradise Street, given in our version, was to the sailor an earthly paradise, where after a long voyage, no man his master, he would stroll ashore, money in his pockets to burn, seeking female company.

Oh, as I wuz a-rol-lin'down Pa-ra-dise Street, Tim-me way, hay, blow the man down! A sas-sy flash clip-per I chanct for to meet, Ooh! Give us some time to blow the man down!

2. This spankin' flash packet she said unto me,
   "There's a dandy full-rigger [Blackballer] just ready for sea."

3. This dandy full-rigger to New York wuz bound,
   She wuz very well rigged and very well found.

4. So I packed up me sea-chest and signed on that day,
   An' with this flash packet I spent me half-pay.

5. 'Twas when this Blackballer wuz ready for sea,
   'Tis then that you'll see such a hell of a spree.

6. There's tinkers an' tailors an' soldiers an' all,
   All ship as prime seamen aboard this Blackball.

7. "Lay aft, here, ye lubbers, lay aft one an' all,
   I'll have none o'yer dodges aboard this Blackball!"

8. An' now when she's clear over ol' Mersey Bar,
   The mate knocks 'em down with a big capstan bar.

9. As soon as this packet is well out to sea,
   There's cruel hard treatment o' every degree.

10. So we'll blow the man up, bullies, blow the man down,
    Wid a crew o'hard cases from Liverpool town!

In our song a sailor takes the advice of his ladylove to join a hard-case outward-bounder, much to his sorrow. The Blackball packets were tough and were avoided by all but the Irish packet rats who made them their home. These Irish seamen consisted of New York and Liverpool Irish, as well as Irish from County this or that. "To blow" means to strike, the chief mate of Blackballers being called the "Blower" and the second mate, the "Striker."

76

HERE'S THE TENDER COMIN'

ENGLISH: FOREBITTER

This song hails from the coaly Tyne area of Britain, one of the British seaboards where the pressgangs plied their nefarious ways. In the days of the Napoleonic Wars the press tenders were ubiquitous. The pressgangs not only worked the taverns and waterfront pubs of the ports, they were just as common inland; at crossroads and rural villages they would lie in wait for their prey. Often referred to as "Lobsters," the pressgang consisted of six to eight men with a "Yellow Admiral," or worn-out lieutenant, in charge. When the "King's Navee" was undermanned they doubled their efforts. The cry of "Press!" was enough to give a scare to any male between the ages of fifteen and sixty.

Here's the ten-der com-ing, press-ing all the men;
Oh, my hin-ny, what shall we do then? Here's the
ten-der com-ing, off at Shield's Bar,
Here's the ten-der com-ing, full of men-o'-war.

2. Hide thee, canny Geordie, hide thyself away,
   Hide thee till the tender makes for Druid's Bay;
   If they catch thee, Geordie, who's to win our bread?
   Me an' little Jacky'd better off be dead.

3. Here's the tender comin', a-stealin' of me dear;
   Oh, my hinny, they'll press ye out o' here;
   They will send ye foreign, that is what this means;
   Here's the tender comin', full o' red marines.

4. Here's the tender comin', pressin' all the men,
   Oh, dear hinny, what shall we do then?
   Here's the tender comin', off at Shield's Bar,
   Here's the tender comin', full o' men-o'-war.

Certain groups of tradesmen – fishermen, Thames watermen, whalers, and so on – were granted "permissions," excusing them from being pressed, but usually the gangs overruled such exemptions. Press tenders would lie off, and on, the estuaries of rivers and the entrances of ports. When a merchant ship or whaler was sighted, the pressgang would board her, taking such a large percentage of the crew that the ship would be unmanageable. Some of the men thus captured may have been on a two-year voyage, with the prospect of another two-year voyage facing them, thus never getting a chance to build up their bodies with green shore food – one of the reasons the Fleet was inflicted with so much scurvy.

77

FLASH GALS OF THE TOWN

ENGLISH: FOREBITTER

This is another of the numerous Ratcliffe Highway type of songs in the old-time sailing-ship sailorman's repertoire, a favorite while sitting on the forebitts in the nor'east tradewinds. The phrase "Nelson's Blood" refers to rum, and sailors tell a yarn about how this came to be so.

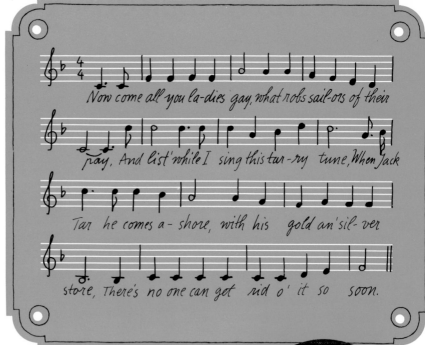

Now come all you ladies gay, what robs sailors of their pay, And list' while I sing this tar-ry tune, When Jack Tar he comes a-shore, with his gold an' sil-ver store, There's no one can get rid o' it so soon.

2. Now the first thing he demands is a fiddler to his hand,
A bottle of Nelson's Blood so stout an' warm,
And a pretty gal likewise with two dark an' rollin' eyes,
An' he'll drop his anchor an' never more will roam.

3. Then the landlady she comes in with her brand new crinoline,
She looks like some bright an' flashin' star,
An' she's ready to wait on him, if his pockets are lined with tin,
An' to chalk his score on the board behind the bar.

4. Then she calls a pretty maid, right-handed an' soft-laid,
An' up aloft they climb without much bother,
An' she shortens in her sail for a weatherin' of the gale,
An' soon in the tiers they're moored quite close together.

5. Then he shifted her main tack an' he caught her flat aback,
They rolled from the lee to the weather,
An' he laid her close 'longside, oh, closehauled as she would lie,
'Twas tack an' tack through hell an' stormy weather.

6. But his money soon was gone, an' his flash gal soon had flown,
She roamed along the Highway for another,
An' the landlady cried, "Pay yer score an' git outside,
Yer cargo's gone an' you've met stormy weather."

7. Then poor ol' Jack must understand that there's ships a-wantin' hands,
And to the Shadwell Basin he went down,
And he shipped away forelorn on a passage round the Horn,
Goodbye to the boys an' the flash gals of the town.

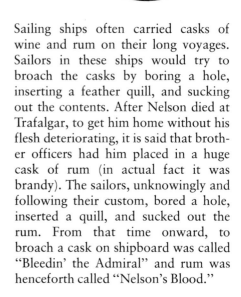

Sailing ships often carried casks of wine and rum on their long voyages. Sailors in these ships would try to broach the casks by boring a hole, inserting a feather quill, and sucking out the contents. After Nelson died at Trafalgar, to get him home without his flesh deteriorating, it is said that brother officers had him placed in a huge cask of rum (in actual fact it was brandy). The sailors, unknowingly and following their custom, bored a hole, inserted a quill, and sucked out the rum. From that time onward, to broach a cask on shipboard was called "Bleedin' the Admiral" and rum was henceforth called "Nelson's Blood."

SINGAPOR-SANG

German: Capstan Song

In many of the training ships of France, Belgium, and Germany, the cadets composed shanties suitable for shipboard work – not traditional ones, but often based on true incidents. The steward's purchase of a bull in this song turned out to be one big headache, an incident which actually occurred aboard the German training ship *Arkona*.

2. *Und kommen wir nach Singapor,*
   Und kommen wir nach Singapor, dann geht der Bottler
   gleich on shore.

3. *Der Bottler kauft dort einen Bull'n,*
   Der Bottler kauft dort einen Bull'n, und macht auf
   dem Kommando Schuld'n.

4. *An der Grossraa wird er aufgeheisst,*
   An der Grossraa wird er aufgeheisst, und auf das
   Achterdeck geschmeisst.

5. *Der Bottler holt ein grosses Knife,*
   Der Bottler holt ein grosses Knife, und geht damit,
   dem Bull zu life.

6. *Der Bulle reisst das Strippchen ab,*
   Der Bulle reisst das Strippchen ab, der Bottler in
   das Want schapp, schapp.

7. *Die Wache kommt nun angerannt,*
   Die Wache kommt nun angerannt, Bullen an dat
   want.

8. *Das End' vom Liede ist nun dies,*
   Das End' vom Liede ist nun dies, der Bulle kommt
   in dem Kombüs.

1. On a long voyage, as you know,
   Ch.: As you know!
   On a long voyage, as you know, the meat we have is tough as leather,
   Ch.: Holderie ya heh, holderie ya heh! Holay!
   (Repeat second line in each verse and second chorus line)

2. And when we come to Singapore,
   Ch.: Singapore!
   And when we come to Singapore, the steward there he goes ashore.

3. The steward there he buys a bull,
   Ch.: Buys a bull!
   The steward there he buys a bull and charges it to the Old Man.

4. And by the mainyard it is hoisted,
   Ch.: It is hoisted!
   And by the mainyard it is hoisted and dropped down on the afterdeck.

5. The steward holds a great big knife,
   Ch.: Great big knife!
   The steward holds a great big knife and goes with it the bull to kill.

6. The bull breaks its lashings off,
   Ch.: Lashings off!
   The bull breaks his lashings off and bumps the steward in the stern.

7. The watch now comes on the run,
   Ch.: On the run!
   The watch now comes on the run and bashed the bull upon its stern.

8. Now the end of the story is this,
   Ch.: It is this!
   Now the end of this sory it is this: The bull finished up in the cabin!

PADDY WEST

ENGLISH: FOREBITTER

Paddy West was a well-known Liverpool boarding-house master of the last century, with a difference. In his house in Great Howard Street he guaranteed he could make a bank-clerk, cowhand, docker, or yokel into an A.B. within a week. As it states in the song, Paddy finally, after teaching him how to steer and to furl a sail, had him "cross the Line" (a piece of string) and "round the Horn" (a bullock's horn) so that the candidate could honestly tell the mate of the ship he shipped aboard that he was an able seaman. The term "Paddy Wester" was still in use in recent times to refer to a useless seaman.

Oh, as I wuz a-rol-lin' down Great How-ard
Street, I stroll'd in to Pad-dy West's house, He-
gave me a plate of A-mer-i-can hash, an'
swore it wuz Eng-lish scouse, Sez he, "Look here, young
fel-ler, yer ver-y just in time, To-go-a-
way in a big dip-per ship, an' ver-y soon ye'll
sign." Then it's put on yer dun-gar-ee jack-et,
CH.
An' give the boys a rest, An'-think o' the
cold-nor'-west-ers that blow in the house o' Pad-dy West's!

2. When I got into ol' Paddy West's house the wind began to blow,
   He sent me up to the lumber-room the fore royal for to stow,
   When I climbed up to the attic, no fore royal could I find,
   So I took a tumble to meself an' I furled the window blind.

3. It's Paddy, me boy, he pipes all hands on deck, their stations for to man,
   His wife, Mary Ann, stood in the back yard, a bucket in her hand.
   His wife let go of the bucket, the water flew on its way,
   "Clew up yer fore t'gall'nt, me sons, she's taken in a sea!"

4. Now Paddy, sez he, "In imagination to the south'ard we are bound,"
   An' he took a long, long piece of string an' he tied it round an' round.
   I stepped across it an' back again, and Paddy sez, "That's fine,
   When the mate he axes 'have ye ever bin ter sea?'
                                Yiz can say ye've crossed the Line."

5. "When he axes if you've ever bin ter sea, don't tell him not till this morn,
   For, be Jasus," sez he, "A sailor ye'll be, from the hour that ye wuz born,
   Just go into the parlour, walk round the bullock's horn,
   An' tell the mate, that ye'ave bin ten times round the Horn!"

SAILORS' GIRLS: FAITHFUL AND FAITHLESS

The romantic idea of a sailor having "a wife in every port" is, of course, extremely euphemistic and nowhere near the truth. Replace "wife" with "harlot" and one is nearer to fact. Having little freedom or money when in a foreign port and knowing little of the lingo, he preferred to stay in the purlieus of sailortown and drink in the "First and Last" pub. French sailors from the Bounty ships, in Chile, weren't allowed ashore, and British tars were usually given only one day's freedom ashore. In his home port the young sailor probably had a sweetheart but poor pay and long absences rarely led to the altar. Although noted more in song than in actual fact, tearful separations of a sailor and his true love did occur – and sometimes the girl concerned wasn't

even a "nice" girl. A story well known in the fo'c'sle tells of a seaman falling in love with a Frisco whore but being prevented from marrying her by his shipmates. On the voyage home he becomes sicker daily from no apparent cause but a broken heart, dying and being buried at sea within sight of his home port.

In the wheat ports of South Australia many a young Swede, Finn, or German seaman jumped ship and married a local farmer's daughter and settled down to farming – an occupation followed on the shores of the Baltic for many generations by his family. "Nice girls," as opposed to sailortown "harpies," were to be found attending dances and concerts given for sailors by

"tin" one at "pretty little Stockton" in Newcastle, N.S.W., where many a young seaman left his heart in the keeping of a rosy-cheeked mission girl. Other well-known missions were the Flying Angel in Buenos Aires, Hardy's in Valparaiso, and the one in Cape Town.

various seamen's missions in ports throughout the world. In Australia the ladies of the Harbour Lights Guild came into this category. It was mostly the impoverished apprentices, cadets, and ships' boys who rolled up at the mission, the harder type of older seaman making for such a haven only when skint of money. A famous mission was the

Sailing-ship masters, if married, would take their wives to sea with them and many a child was born aboard nineteenth-century windjammers. Some wives of New England sperm-whaling captains used to sail with their husbands, but more often they had to wait at home for three years for their husband's return from the South Pacific. To this day are to be seen in Nantucket, New Bedford, Sag Harbor, and other erstwhile whaling ports, the "widows' walks" atop the clapboard houses, where the so-called widow would sit or pace, awaiting the return of a roving husband.

GANGSPILLIEDJE

DUTCH: CAPSTAN SONG

This shanty is one of the few surviving Dutch shanties; like most of the others it comes from Terschelling, the third from the west of the West Frisian Islands. Only small fishing boats actually belong to Terschelling; but many of her sons, in years gone by, went to sea in deepwatermen.

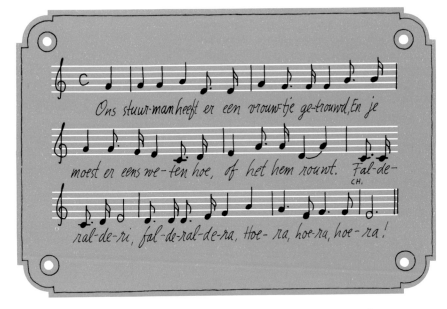

Ons stuur-man heeft er een vrouw-tje ge-trouwd, En je moest er eens we-ten hoe, of het hem rouwt. Fal-de-ral-de-ri, fal-de-ral-de-ra, Hoe-ra, hoe-ra, hoe-ra!

GANGWAY SONG

2. Want kousen stoppen dat kan ze niet,
   En eten koken een groot verdriet.

3. O, Stuurman, kom eens met de fles,
   En geef ons de man een borrel of zes.

4. Een borrel of zes is wel wat veel,
   Maar geef ons danmaar twee voor ons deel.

5. O, Stuurman, kom dan maar met de kruik,
   En geef ons maar één voor ons gebruik.

1. Our mate has married a wife,
   And you ought to know how he regrets it.
   Ch.: Falderal-deri, falderal-dera,
   hurrah, hurrah, hurrah!

2. She's no good at mending stockings,
   And makes a hash of cooking meals.

3. Oh, mate, come with your bottle,
   And give each man a dram or six.

4. A dram or six is rather much,
   Well, give us each two drams only.

5. Oh, mate, bring us your jar,
   And give us one dram only.

It is a typical hauling shanty in so far as there is no special sequence to the verses. Anything or everything could be taken by a good shantyman who had the knack of improvisation and be made into extra verses to lengthen out the song when the hoist was particularly long.

THE HANDSOME CABIN BOY

ENGLISH: FOREBITTER

The story of a girl dressing as a man and going to sea is a fairly common one among nautical annals. The first woman to circumnavigate the globe was a Frenchwoman aboard one of Bougainville's frigates in his round-the-world voyage in 1766. She was called Jeanne Baré. Other women who dressed as sailors and went to sea – either to follow their sweethearts or husbands, or just to satisfy their love of adventure – were Ann Mills, Anne Chamborlayne, an English girl calling herself Arthur Douglas, an Irish girl Hannah Whitney, and of course the pirates Anne Bonny and Mary Read.

Now, 'tis of a hand-some fe-e-male as you should un-der-stand, She had a mind for rov-ing un-to some fo-reign land, At-tired in sail-or's cloth-ing, she bold-ly did ap-pear, And en—gaged— with a cap-tain, to serve him for a year.

2. She engaged with a captain, a cabin boy to be.
The wind it being in favor they proudly put to sea.
The captain's lady being on board she seemed in great joy,
To think the captain had engaged a handsome cabin boy.

3. So gentle was this pretty maid, she did her duty well;
Then what followed next, me boys, the song itself will tell:
The captain and this pretty maid did oftimes kiss and toy,
For he soon found out the secret of the handsome cabin boy.

4. Her cheeks were like the rosebuds and her sidelocks all in curl;
The sailors often smiled and said he looks just like a girl.
Through eating cabin biscuits her color did destroy,
And the waist did swell of pretty Nell, the handsome cabin boy.

5. As through the Bay o' Biscay our gallant ship did plow,
One night among the sailors there was an awful row;
They tumbled from their hammocks, it did their rest destroy,
They swore it was the groaning of the handsome cabin boy.

6. "Oh, doctor! Oh, doctor!" the cabin boy did cry;
The sailors swore by all that's good the cabin boy would die.
The doctor he came runnin'–a-smilin' at the fun,
To think the sailor boy would have a daughter or a son.

7. Now when the sailors heard the joke, they all began to stare;
"The child belongs to none of us," they solemnly did swear.
The lady to the captain said, "My dear, I wish you joy,
It's either you or I betrayed the handsome cabin boy!"

DAAR WAS EENS EEN MEISJE LOOS

DUTCH: BALLAST-STOWING SHANTY

This song – built on the pattern of an English hauling shanty – was used for stowing ballast into the holds of Dutch ships. Another version, with a different tune and without refrains, is said to be a rather common song among Dutch schoolchildren. In their version, however the story is said to finish with verse seven. This song, too, comes from Terschelling but was also known on the island of Wieringen (North Holland).

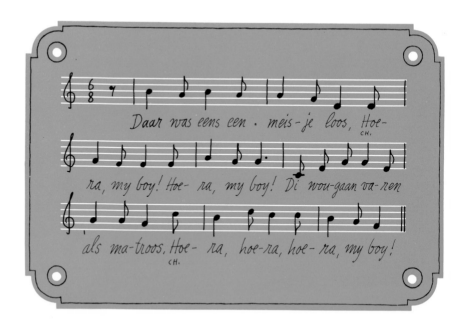

Daar was eens een meis-je loos, Hoe-ra, my boy! Hoe- ra, my boy! Di wou-gaan va-ren als ma-troos. Hoe- ra, hoe-ra, hoe-ra, my boy!

This song came to me, like the other Dutch shanties in this volume, through the kindness of my friends K. Suyk and Kees Hos. It is, of course, one of the numerous songs of girls going to sea, although it isn't clear in this case whether she went as an ordinary female mariner or in disguise as a man.

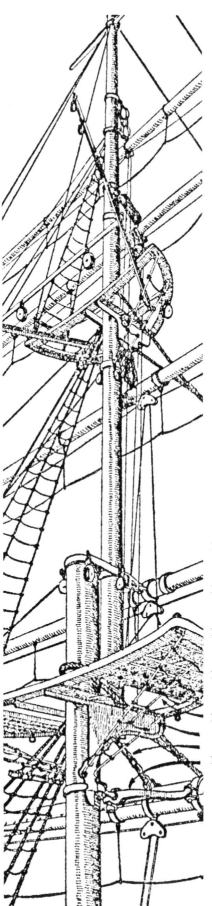

2. Zij nam dienst voor zeven jaar,
   Omdat zij vreesde voor geen gevaar.

3. Zij bracht haar kist en koffer aan boord,
   Gelijk een jonge matroos behoort.

4. Zij moest toen klimmen inde mast,
   Maken de zeilen met touwen vast.

5. Maar door zwaar storm en onweer,
   Sloegen de zeilen van boven neer.

6. Zij werd gebonden aan de mast,
   Al met haar handen en voeten vast.

7. Zij riep: "Kapteintje, sla mij niet,
   Ik ben uw liefje, zoals gij ziet."

8. En daad'lijk werd ze los gemaakt,
   Al met een kusje werd ze geraakt.

9. Zij moest toen komen in de kajuit,
   Trekken matrozenkleren uit.

10. En wat er in de kajuit is geschied,
    Dat weet de eerste stuurman niet.

11. Maar eer her scheepje was aan wal,
    Was er 't jonge matroosje al.

12. Toen zij nu weer kwam in de stad,
    Waar zij (nog) een moeder had.

13. Riep zij: "Moeder, word niet boos,
    Ik heb gevaren voor jong matroos."

14. "Bij een, die mij sprecht bemint,
    Heb ik dit klein (e) onnozel kind."

15. "Maar eer het tweede Pinkster is,
    Ben ik zijn vrouwtje, dat is gewis."

ONCE THERE WAS A CRAFTY GIRL

1. Once there was a crafty girl,
   Ch.: Hurrah, my boy! Hurrah, my boy!
   Who wanted to go sailing as ordinary seaman,
   Ch.: Hurrah, hurrah, hurrah, my boy!

2. She took service for seven years,
   Because she didn't fear any danger.

3. She brought her chest and gear aboard,
   Like a young sailor should.

4. Then she had to climb aloft,
   Furling the sails with gaskets.

5. But a heavy gale and thunderstorm,
   Tore the sails from her hands.

6. They tied her to the mast,
   With her hands and feet fastened.

7. She called: "Captain, don't strike me,
   I'm your lover, can't you see?"

8. And at that moment they unfastened her,
   And she was touched with a kiss.

9. Then she went into the cabin,
   Taking off her sailor clothes.

10. And what happened in the cabin,
    That the first mate does not know.

11. But before the ship reached shore,
    A new young sailor had arrived.

12. And, when she came into the town,
    Where her mother lived,

13. She called: "Mother don't get angry,
    I've sailed as a young seaman."

14. "With one who loves me true,
    I have this innocent, little child."

15. "But before it is Whitmonday,
    I'll be his husband, that's for sure!"

CAWSAND BAY

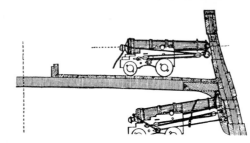

ENGLISH: FOREBITTER

This is a song of fair age and is, I feel, of naval origin – Cawsand Bay being a well-known rendezvous of the British naval fleet. I should say it dates back to the early eighteenth century, judging from the clothes in which Elinor Ford dresses her young sailor.

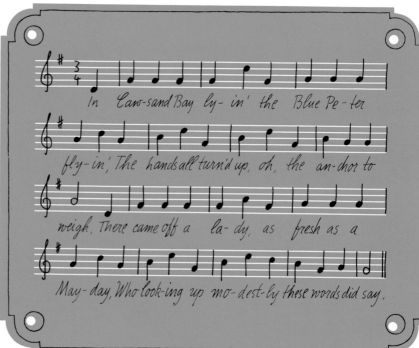

In Cawsand Bay lyin' the Blue Peter flyin', The hands all turn'd up, oh, the anchor to weigh, There came off a lady, as fresh as a Mayday, Who looking up modestly these words did say,

Also the reference to a naval "first-rater" shows that the song cannot be of a much earlier date. It was at about the end of the seventeenth century that a code called "The Establishment" was inaugurated in the British Navy. It governed every part of the building of the hull and the type of rigging to be used, as well as the selection of guns to suit the hull. With the introduction of this ruling the word "rate" was used to signify a special type of ship. A first-rater carried 90–100 guns, a second-rater over 80 and a third-rater over 50. All these rates were considered to be "ships of the line." The fifth and sixth rates were deemed "frigates."

2. "Oh, aloft there an' a hand there, aye, I want a young man there,
   So hoist me aboard or send him to me,
   For his name's Harry Grady, an' I am a lady,
   Just come off to save him from goin' to sea."

3. The captain his honor, when he looked upon her,
   Swung down the ship's side to help her aboard,
   Saying then, with emotion, "What son-o'-the-ocean,
   Can thus be a-wanted by Elinor Ford?"

4. To this she made answer, "That there is me man, sir,
   I'll make him as rich an' us grand as a lord."
   "Look 'ere," sez the captain, "it can't very well 'appen,
   We've got sailing orders. My man, git aboard!"

5. "Avast!" sez the lady, "don't mind him Hal Grady,
   He once was your capen but now you're at large,
   You shan't sail aboard her, in spite that chap's order."
   An' out of her bosom she lugged his discharge.

6. Then the captain, says he, now, "I'm damned but he's free now."
   Hal sings out, "Let Weatherface have all me clothes!"
   For the shore then he steered her, the lads they all cheered her,
   But the captain was jealous an' looked down his nose.

7. Then she got a shore tailor to rig her young sailor,
   In tight nankeen britches an' a long, blue-tailed coat;
   He looked like a squire for all to admire,
   Wid a dimity handkerchief tied round his throat.

8. An' now she says, "Harry - the next thing we'll marry,"
   An' she looked like a dove in his far manly face,
   "That's good," says Hal Grady, "a parson stand ready,
   An' after a long splice we'll splice the main brace."

9. An' they got a house, greater than e'er a first-rater,
   Wid lackeys in uniform servin' the drinks;
   Wid a garden to go in, wid flowers a-flowin':
   The lily, the tulip, the lilac, an' pink.

10. Then he got eddication, quite fit for his station,
    'Cos ye know we ain't never too old for to larn,
    An' his shipmates soon found him, wid the young uns around him,
    All chips off the old block, from stem to the starn.

PASSANT PAR PARIS

FRENCH: CAPSTAN SHANTY

This capstan song has the typical French method of forming choruses, by the hands singing a repeat of the first solo, and then using the second solo as the first solo of the following verse. In this shanty the translation has been toned down a little. Many of these French shanties – particularly the capstan ones – are, musically speaking, much superior, I feel, to those of Anglo-Saxon seamen, some almost reaching operatic standards.

Pas-sant par Pa-ris, vi-dant ma bou-tei-lle,
Pas-sant par Par-ris, vi-dant ma bou-tei-lle, Un de
mes a-mis me dit à l'or-ei-lle, Bon! Bon! Bon!
Le bon vin m'en-dort, l'a-mour me ré-vei-lle,
Le bon vin m'en-dort, l'a-mour me ré-veill'en-cor'!

2. Un de mes amis me dit à l'oreille,
   Jean, prends garde à toi, l'on courtis'ta belle.

3. Jean, prends garde à toi, l'on courtis'ta belle,
   Courtise qui voudra, je me fous bien d'elle!

4. Courtise qui voudra, je me fous bien d'elle,
   J'ai eu de son coeur, la fleur la plus belle.

5. J'ai eu de son coeur, la fleur la plus belle,
   Dans un grand lit blanc, gréé de dentelles.

6. Dans un grand lit blanc, gréé de dentelles,
   J'ai eu trois garçons, tous trois capitaines.

7. J'ai eu trois garçons, tous trois capitaines,
   L'un est à Bordeaux, l'autre à La Rochelle.

8. L'un est à Bordeaux, l'autre à La Rochelle,
   Le plus jeune à Paris, courtisant les belles.

9. Le plus jeune à Paris, courtisant les belles,
   Et le père est ici, qui hal' sur la ficelle.

92

PASSING THROUGH PARIS

1. Passing through Paris, knocking back the bottle,
   Ch.: Passing through Paris, knocking back the bottle,
   One of my friends whispered in my ear,
   Ch.: Good! Good! Good!
   The good wine makes me sleep, but love wakes me up,
   Ch.: The good wine makes me sleep, but love wakes me up.

2. One of my friends whispered in my ear,
   John, take care, somebody's courting your girl.
   (Repeat third line, above, in each verse)

3. John, take care, somebody's courting your girl,
   Anyone can court her, I don't give a damn for her.

4. Anyone can court her, I don't give a damn for her,
   I have had the finest flower of her heart.

5. I have had the finest flower of her heart,
   In a big white bed trimmed with lace.

6. In a big white bed trimmed with lace,
   I have had three boys, all captains.

7. I have had three boys, all captains,
   One is in Bordeaux, the other at La Rochelle.

8. One is in Bordeaux, the other at La Rochelle,
   The youngest is in Paris, courting the girls.

9. The youngest is in Paris, courting the girls,
   And the father is here, hauling on the string.

Å KOM TILL MIG PÅ LÖRDAAG KVALL

SWEDISH:
WINDLASS AND CAPSTAN SHANTY

Captain Sternvall, who is the source for this song, says that it is an old working song used at one time in Swedish ports when loading or discharging cargo. He states that there are eighteen verses in all, but that most are not suitable for publication since they refer to the "eighteen points of feeling in the body." This version was first written down by Captain Olof Olsson on *Råå*.

COME TO ME
ON SATURDAY NIGHT

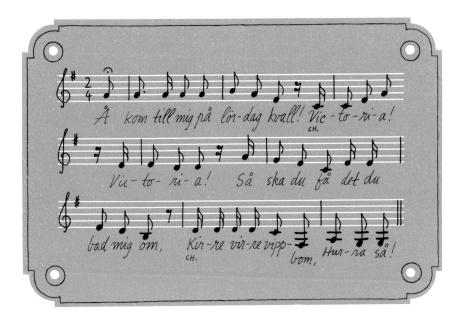

Å kom till mig på lör-dag kvall! Vic-to-ri-a! *CH.*
Vic-to-ri-a! Så ska du få det du
bad mig om, Kir-re vir-re vipp- *CH.* bom, Hur-ra så!

2. *Nej, jag törs inte gå till dig,*
   För far dins hunder biter mig.

3. *Den svarta hunden den är död,*
   Den vita ger du en bit bröd.

4. *Och när du kommer i kammarn in,*
   Dar står en flaska brännevin.

5. *Då tar du dig en duktig sup,*
   Så du kan stå bataljen ut.

1. Come to me on Saturday night,
   Ch.: Victoria! Victoria!
   An' you will get your wants alright,
   Ch.: Cherry-cherry, vip-bom, hurra so!

2. Oh, no, I dare not go to thee,
   Thy father's dogs they will bite me.

3. The big, black dog, well it is dead,
   And to the white one give some bread.

4. And when you come into my room,
   You'll find some brandy to consume.

5. Just take a deep swig at the bottle,
   So you'll be ready for the battle.

STORMY WINTER'S NIGHT

ENGLISH: FOREBITTER

This is in the vein of the sad, sentimental songs prevalent ashore in England in Queen Victoria's reign. According to my mother, my grandfather – a ship's carpenter – would sing this heartstring-pulling ditty after every Christmas dinner. The leaving of home and loved-ones was a common situation in the days of sail. Merchant and naval seamen would be away for months and whalers sometimes for years and, of course, as in the song, many never returned. Deaths aboard merchant ships were due, mainly, to falling from aloft or to scurvy. In naval ships, fever (typhus), dysentery (due to drinking foul beer), and scurvy, in peacetime, took their toll; while in wartime, death was mainly due to enemy action.

It was a storm-y win-ter's night, the snow lay on the ground; A sail-or boy stood on the quay, his ship was out-ward bound. His sweet-heart stand-ing by his side, shed many a bit-ter tear; And as he pressed her to his breast, he whis-pered in her ear.

Ch.: Farewell, farewell, my own true love,
This parting gives me pain;
You'll be my own true guiding star,
Till I return again.
My thoughts will ever be of you,
When storms are raging high;
Farewell, farewell, remember me,
Your faithful sailor boy!

2. 'Twas in a gale, the ship set sail, his sweetheart standing by.
She watched the ship far out of sight, till tears had dimmed her eye;
She prayed to God in heaven above, to guide him on his way,
And then those parting words she heard, an echoing over the bay.

3. Sad to say the ship returned without the sailor boy;
He died while on the voyage home; the flag was half-mast high.
And when his shipmates came ashore, they told her he was dead;
And in a letter that he wrote, these last lines sadly said:

It is said that the English fleet at the battle of the Armada lost far more men from disorders caused by drinking polluted beer than from enemy shot; and Admiral Anson, on his world voyage in the 1740s, lost the greater portion of his men from scurvy.

94

HAUL AWAY, OLD FELLOW, AWAY

FRENCH: HALYARD SHANTY

This is another hauling song popular with Jean Matelot. It has as its theme the fact that "ladies of quality" are above the *garces des quais*, the common or garden-variety sailor's girls.

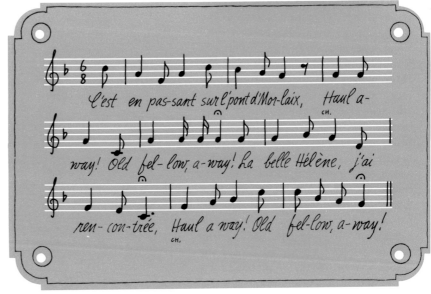

C'est en pas-sant sur l'pont d'Mor-laix, Haul a-way! Old fel-low, a-way! La belle Hélène, j'ai ren-con-trée, Haul a way! Old fel-low, a-way!

Our hero knows his place – he should not be deigning to try his luck with such a lady; for him the common trollop, the whores of the wharfside of sailortown. Many sailorsongs have this theme. On the other hand there are those songs in which Jack (or Jean or Jan) manages to outwit the type of gallant that such a lady of quality, under normal circumstances, prefers – someone of her own class – and he manages, by subterfuge, to get the dainty lady into his arms.

In this latter class of song we have: "Do Me Amma," "Jack the Jolly Tar," and "Yarmouth Town."

2. Bien humblement j'l'ai saluée,
   D'un doux sourire ell'm'a remercié.

3. Mais j'ai bien vu qu'c'est charité,
   Car c'est une dame de qualité.

4. C'est la fille d'un cap'taine nantais,
   Un matelot ne s'ra jamais.

5. Pour nous sont les garces des quais,
   Qui vol'nt, qui mentent, qui font tuer!

6. J'n'étale plus, j'vas tout larguer,
   J'vas faire mon trou dans l'a salée.

7. Mat'lots, mon coeur est embrumé,
   Buvons quand même a sa beauté.

8. Encore un coup pour étarquer,
   Hisse le grand foc! Tout est payé!

1. When I was crossing the bridge of Morlaix,
   Ch.: Haul away! Old fellow, away!
   I met Helen looking so gay,
   Ch.: Haul away! Old fellow, away!

2. With me hat in me hand I said, "How d'ya do?"
   She gave me a smile that said, "Thank you!"

3. Her smile I could see was merely charity,
   'Cos she was a lady of quality.

4. The daughter, me lads, of a Nantes captain,
   She'll never belong to a simple sailor.

5. For us the trollops who hang round the quay,
   Who lie an' steal, get men killed with glee.

6. No longer I'll stick it, cast off everything,
   I'm going to ship deepwater.

7. Shipmates, me heart is wrapped in a fog,
   Let's drink, all the same, to her beauty in grog.

8. One more pull lads, oh, haul her away,
   Hoist taut the big jib – high enough, belay!

95

DE IJZERE MAN

DUTCH: CAPSTAN SONG

Captain Spaandarman, over eighty years of age, gave this shanty to my friend Mr. K. Suyk. The captain said: "The first steamer of the Nederlands Steam Navigation Company (now the Holland-America line) was rigged as a brig, with two square-rigged masts. She still had an old-fashioned man-handled capstan. The ship lay in the roads at Hellevoetsluis, about to make her first passage to America. Her ex-sailing-ship hands raised the anchor to this shanty. Later I joined the bark *Senior*, aboard which sailed some members of the Dutch steamer already mentioned, and when this sailing ship was at anchor in False Bay, near the Cape of Good Hope, we signaled for a tug to take us to Cape Town.

"We had sixty fathoms of chain out and when we came to weigh anchor, the 'Iron Man' was the shanty we raised." The "Baggerman" mentioned in the shanty was a public house run by a certain Mr. Baggerman, who had several daughters. In the old days before the Canal was cut through, ships would lie in the roads at Helle-voetsluis instead of going up to Rotter-dam. The crimps would bring the crews out in small boats from the boarding houses of Rotterdam's Schedamschedyk. This shanty has been bowdlerized.

In Hel-le-voets-luis daar staat een huis, Hoe-ra die ij-ze-re man! Daar zijn de da-mes van Bag-ger-man thuis, Hoe-ra die ij-ze-re man! Dan zin-gen wij vro-lijk fal-de-ral-de-ra, wie gaat er met ons mee? Wij va-ren naar A-me-ri-ka, het schip ligt op de ree, Wij va-ren naar A-me-ri-ka, het schip ligt op de ree!

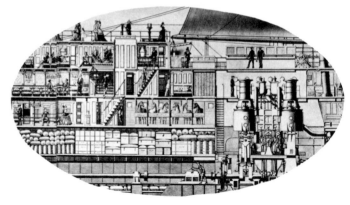

96

THE IRON MAN

1. At Hellevoetsluis there stands a house,
   Ch.: Hurrah the Iron Man!
   There the Baggerman damsels, they are at home.
   Ch.: Hurrah the Iron Man!
   Then we'll sing merrily – falderal-dera, who's coming with us now?
   We are sailing for America, the ship lies in the roads,
   We are sailing for America, the ship lies in the roads!

2. *En in dat huis daar staat een stok,*
   Daar krijgen de dames mee op hun kop.

3. *Een juffrouw die naar de kerk wou gaan,*
   Die liet haar hoofd met goud beslaan.

4. *Aan ieder haar had zij een bel,*
   Het was gelijk een klokkespel.

5. *En toen zij dan de kerk in gang,*
   Toen gingen die bellen van ring ting ting.

6. *De Dominee die op zijn preekstoel zat,*
   Die dacht U wee wat een wijf is dat.

7. *De koster die dit werk bezag,*
   Die was van streek de hele dag.

8. *De dienstmeid die dit werk bekeek,*
   Die was jaloers de hele week.

9. *En die dit lied al heeft gedicht,*
   Die kan er rijmen zonder licht.

2. And in that house there is a stick,
   With it the girls on their heads are hit.

3. One girl to church; oh, she wished to go,
   She had her head all set with gold.

4. And on each hair she put a bell,
   The noise was like a carillon.

5. And when she entered into church,
   The bells all ringing, up the aisle she lurched.

6. The vicar in his pulpit there,
   To himself he thought, what a damsel fair.

7. The verger looked at this strange sight,
   He felt upset all day and night.

8. The serving maid who saw her there,
   Was jealous of her golden hair.

9. And he who wrote these verses fine,
   In the dark can make up any rhyme.

DET BLÅSER KALLT, KALLT VÄDER IFRAN SJÖN

SWEDISH: PUMPING SONG

This ditty was sung at the pumps and it dates from the end of the nineteenth century. Judging from the words, it was probably sung aboard the smaller wooden barks of 300–600 tons, which engaged in the coasting trade of the Baltic Sea.

Kalmar is a small port on the western side of Kalmar Sound; the island of Öland is opposite. In the past it was a famous sailing-ship port, one of many small places – Gavle, Norrkö, Märnöstrand, Söderhamn, Malmö, and so on – from which the Baltic barks took their cargoes, oftentimes lumber, to various North European harbors. Many of these small wooden ships were built locally in Sweden and in Norway.

Å när som jag var på mitt fjor-ton de år,
Det blå-ser kallt vä-der i-från sjön! Då
bör-ja jag att seg-la på böl-jor-na de blå, Det
blå-ser kallt, kallt vä-der i-från sjön!

2. A när som jag seglat en månad eller två,
Så var jag lika aktad som kaptenens egen son.

3. A när som vi kom intill Kalmare hamn,
Vi bärga våra segel och hala oss i land.

4. A när som jag kom upp till Kalmare torg,
Da stod där samma flicka med en grönmålad korg.

5. A när som jag kom ut till Kalmare tull,
Så stod där samma flicka så om och kärleksfull.

6. A då sade jag till flickan som så,
"Säg, vill du mig giva en kyss eller två?"

7. "Nej tack, min gunstig herre, jag kysser inte er,
Ty om ni fått en så vill ni ha fler."

8. Men se då tog jag den flickan allt uti min famm,
Och bar henne ned till Kalmare hamn.

9. Å nu så a vi gifta, å nu så ä hon min,
Ty jag fick taga min, när de andra tagit sin.

10. Å hade jag makten och denna vore min,
Så skulle alla flickor i burar lasas in.

11. Å hade jag makten och denna vore min,
Så skulle alla gossarna ha nycklarna dit in.

12. Å den som sjunger visan och inte lägger till,
Han plikte fem riksdaler och miste flickan sin.

1. Oh, 'twas when I was in my fourteenth year,
   Ch.: The cold weather's blowin' in from sea!
   Then I began to sail over the billows so blue,
   Ch.: The cold, cold weather's blowin' in from sea!

2. And when I'd sailed for a month or two,
   I was respected as the captain's own son.

3. Oh, when we sailed into Kalmar's harbor,
   We took in all sail and then warped the ship to shore.

4. Oh, when I came out on to Kalmar's market,
   There stood a girl with a green-painted basket.

5. Oh, when I came out to Kalmar's toll-gate,
   The same girl stood there, so willing a mate.

6. Oh, then I said to the girl like this,
   Say will you not give me just one little kiss?

7. No thanks, my fine fellow, I will not kiss you,
   For if you get one, so will you have two.

8. Buth then I took this girl into my heart,
   And carried her down to Kalmar's port.

9. So now we are married, oh, so now she is mine,
   For I got mine where ye all had taken thine.

10. Oh, had I the power like old-time sages,
    The girls would be all locked up in cages.

11. Oh, had I the power and it was mine,
    All the lads would get keys to admit them.

12. He who sings this song and will not put into port,
    He forfeits five riks-dollars and nevermore will court.

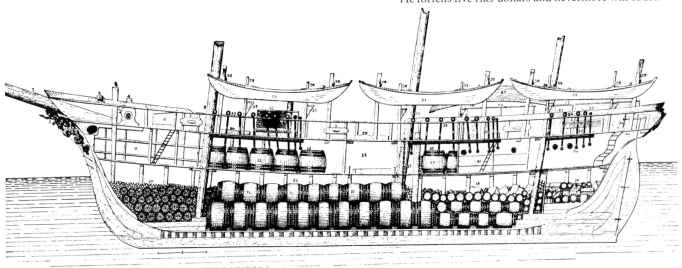

SKÖN JUNGFRUN
HON GÅNGAR SIG TILL HÖGSTA BERG

SWEDISH: PUMPING SHANTY

The refrain in this song is a repeat of the first two lines. Captain Sternvall writes: "In spite of its simple melody, it is not so easy to sing – the scansion must be helped out. It is a lengthy ballad; in some versions it is the bride who smooths her hair, the boy who pales and the girl who, at last, suffers the dreadful fate." He also states that "some seamen's versions are not so nice."

This song is what is known in folk circles as a "token song" – in which the sailor leaves a gold ring with his loved one, as a mark he will soon return. Its theme is somewhat like that of the French shanty "Retour du Marin," except that in the latter the sailor goes back to his ship, whereas here he commits suicide.

THE PRETTY MAID CLIMBS UP
THE HIGHEST MOUNTAIN

2. Den yngsta, den minstaste gossen,
   Som uppå det skeppet var,
   Han ville med junfrun trolova sig,
   Så ung som han ännu var.

3. När gossen skulle bortsegla,
   Till en främmande strand,
   Så tog han upp gullringar fem,
   Och satte på jungfruns hand.

4. När gossen var bortrester,
   Tog jungfrun en annan vän,
   Den gossen som hon lovat tro,
   Den älskade hon ej mer.

5. När tre år voro förgångna,
   Kom gossen hem igen,
   Då han kommer till sin faders gård,
   Han frågar hur kärestan mår.

6. "Vi har du så länge levt borta,
   I dag står din käresta brud,
   Ty vi hava båd hört och sport,
   Att du skulle vara död."

7. Så gångar han sig i kammaren in,
   Han kämmar och krusar sitt hår,
   Gångar så hän till bröllopsgård,
   Ser bruden framför sig stå.

8. "Sag, hava de nu för dig ljugit,
   Och sagt att jag var död,
   Så skall det ej vara en timme till,
   Förrn du ser min djupa nöd."

9. Gossen han gångar i kammaren in,
   Slår dörren i lås efter sig,
   Så sätter han sig ned att skriva,
   Ett rörande avskedsbrev.

10. När brevet det nu var skrivet,
    Och timmen var runnen förbi,
    Då drager han fram sin förgyllande kniv,
    Och stöter den i sitt liv.

11. "Gud nåde mig, armaste flicka, nu,
    För den gärning som jag gjort,
    Den ena är jag nu vigder vid,
    Den andra simmar i blod."

1. The pretty maid climbs up the highest mountain,
   To look out over the foaming sea,
   (Repeat first two lines in each verse)
   Then she could see a rolling ship,
   Which sailed upon the sea.

2. The youngest, the very smallest boy,
   Who was on board that ship,
   He would with the maid betrothed be,
   Although he was still so young.

3. When the lad should sail away,
   To a far foreign shore,
   So he took up five golden rings,
   To place on the maiden's hand.

4. When the lad had sailed away,
   The maid took another friend,
   The lad to whom she gave her pledge,
   She loved him now no more.

5. When three long years had passed away,
   The boy came home again,
   When he came home to his father's farm,
   He asked how his sweetheart was.

6. "Now, you have been away many years,
   Today your sweetheart will be a bride,
   For we have both heard and thought,
   That you were long since dead."

7. So he went into his bedroom,
   Where he combed and oiled his hair,
   Then he went to the wedding place,
   Saw the bride before him stand.

8. "So, they have been lying to you,
   And said that I was dead,
   So it will not be but one more hour,
   Ere you see my deep distress."

9. The boy he went into his own chamber,
   And locked the door behind him,
   So he sat himself down for to write,
   A moving farewell letter.

10. When the letter at last was written,
    And the hour had ticked away,
    Then the lad drew forth his fine, golden knife,
    And thrust it into his waist.

11. "God forgive me," said the poor girl,
    "For the deed that I have done,
    The one man I am now married to,
    The other swims in blood."

MADELEINE

BELGIAN/FRENCH: CAPSTAN

We have mentioned elsewhere how the sailors of training ships in France, Germany, and elsewhere sang shanties especially composed by their own crews, often by their own officers or seamen. This is one such shanty, for which we have to thank Commandant LeMaître, one-time captain of the Belgian four-masted bark *L'Avenir*, a beautiful white-painted vessel still around in the 1930s.

"Madeleine" was the special capstan shanty of the Navire-Ecole Belge Company's ship the *Comte de Smet de Nayer*. The original shanty has more verses but we've had to eliminate some owing to their rather bawdy content.

2. *Je lui demand' son nom,*
   Je m'appelle Madeleine,

3. *Je lui lève son jupon,*
   J'aperçois une fontaine,

4. *J'y fais boire mon pinson,*
   Trente-six fois sans perdre haleine,

5. *Quand vous irez à Beaumont,*
   N'oubliez pas Madeleine,

1. Going back in dreams to Beaumont,
   Ch.: La digue, digue, daine,
       La digue, digue, don, don!
   I ran into a virgin,
   Ch.: Digue don, digue don, daine!
   I ran into a virgin,
   Ch.: Aux oiseaux, aux oiseaux!

2. I asked her name,
   I am called Madeleine.
   (Repeat second line in each verse)

3. I lifted up her petticoat,
   And caught sight of a fountain.

4. A bullfinch had a drink there,
   Twenty-six times without drawing air.

5. When you go to Beaumont,
   Don't forget Madeleine.

SALLY BROWN

AMERICAN/ENGLISH:
WINDLASS AND CAPSTAN

It is believed that this song had its birth in the West Indies. It was probably introduced to British ships by way of the West Indiamen that traded, for sugar and rum, with Jamaica and Barbados and other islands of the Caribbean. They brought their cargoes mainly to Bristol, or to the Bristol Channel ports, and to Liverpool and Glasgow.

Ooh! Sal-ly Brown, she's a bright mu-lat-ter,
Way-ay-----, roll an' go! She drinks rum an'
chaws ter-back-er, Spend my mo-ney on Sal-ly Brown!

2. Sally lives on the old plantation,
   She is a daughter of the Wild Goose Nation.

3. Seven long years I courted Sally,
   But all she did was dilly-dally.

4. Sally Brown, what is the matter?
   Pretty gal, but can't get at her.

5. I call her my ol' Queen o' Faces,
   Bought her coral beads and laces.

6. Sally Brown I took a notion,
   To sail across the flamin' ocean.

7. I shipped away in a New Bedford whaler,
   When I got back she wuz courtin' a tailor.

8. Now me troubles they are over,
   Sally's married to a big, black soger.

Sally Brown may or may not have lived, but in any case for the sailor she symbolized all the black or mulatto girls, in their multi-colored, long skirts (with bustles) and their gaudy bandanas fastened in a great butterfly knot atop their heads. They were the girls who met the incoming seamen in Kingston, Bridgetown, and elsewhere, and filled the grog-shops and dancehalls; and Sailor John loved her. Actually there are many shanties based on Sally Brown and/or her daughter. The "Wild Goose Nation" in the song probably came into shantydom by way of Irish seamen who remembered the historical incident when, during England's many attempts to subdue the Irish, certain Irishmen left Ireland to fight as mercenaries on the Continent instead of being forced to soldier under the British flag. This incident was known as "The Flight of the Wild Geese."

ROSABELLA FREDOLIN

SWEDISH: CAPSTAN SONG

The words of this song were often fitted to the hauling song "Ane Madam." The author of *Sång Under Segel* writes about this shanty: "This is a very unusual song; it can be traced for nearly one hundred years in its different variations. This version is from Lars Erik Sandin's songbook, dated 1844.... one immediately recognizes the third verse which deals with the unlucky letters Rosabella uses as hair-curlers. These words are often found in *rallar* (railway) worksongs."
As in America, many of the songs sung by the Swedish railway gangs, in the latter part of the nineteenth century, were picked up by seamen and made into shanties.

2. Jag reste bort och avsked tog,
   Och snarligen hon mig bedrog,
   Det synes väl vad hon mig gav,
   Som kunde en annans hjärta ta.

3. Dom breven jag till henne skrev,
   Hon alla dem i stycken rev,
   Hon vecklade dem uti sitt hår,
   Och detta haver gjort mitt hjärta sar.

4. En repslagardotter är det som,
   Jag denna visa sjunger om,
   Hon håller dans och det förmår,
   Hon jämt på golvet med flaskan går.

5. Och henne är det skickat till,
   Att man må komma när man vill,
   Hon har all ting tillagade,
   Tobak och pipa får man dar.

6. Nu sjunger jag min avskedssång,
   Och flickor tack för denna gång,
   Kom sjöman, håll dig munter och käck,
   Och drick sedan flickornas griller väck.

1. A sailor's greatest delight is,
   Ch.: Fredolin.
   Oh to love a pretty girl, ha, ha,
   Ch.: Fredolin.
   But if she shows herself to be false,
   Oh, she shall have no joy for me,
   Ch.: Rosabella Fredolin!

2. I sailed away and said farewell,
   And all too soon she me betrayed.
   It is well seen what she gave me,
   Who could get hold of another's heart.

3. Those letters which I wrote to her,
   She tore them all into small bits;
   She made them into hair curlers,
   And, oh, that has really made my heart ache.

4. A ropemaker's daughter is she whom
   I am singing this song about.
   She likes to dance and it's sure
   She'll end on the floor with a bottle.

5. And to her is this directed,
   That one can come there when one will.
   She has everything ready;
   Tobacco and pipe one finds there.

6. Now I am singing my farewell song,
   And thank all the girls for this time.
   Come, seamen, keep up your good spirits
   And drink up since the girls' fancies awake.

JULIA

NORWEGIAN: BOWLINE SHANTY

The original collector of this short shanty – Miss Laura Smith (1888) – calls it a "bowline shanty," but the source from which I had it said it was more likely to have been used either at the capstan or pumps. The melody has a marked resemblance to the German shanty "Jub-hei-di, Jub-hei-da." If it was sung as a bowline song it would probably have had one pull in each refrain, with every alternate line being a refrain. On the other hand, it may have had only one pull (as in "Haul the Bowline" or "Haul Away, Joe!") coming on the last word, "Julia!"

A sailor's greatest pleasure,
Ch.: Is Julia! Julia hops as a jo!
Beloved of all the girls so dear,
Ch.: Julia hops as a jo!
Full ch.: Julia, Julia, Julia, Julia hops as a jo!
  Julia, Julia, sweet Julia!

MIN MAND HAN VAR EN SJÖMAND

SWEDISH: HALYARD SHANTY

The source for this song says it is a halyard shanty, but that is difficult to accept. Many Scandinavian and German shanties repeat the verse as a chorus, but there is not even the suggestion of a chorus in this song. Perhaps it was sung by all hands as a hand-over-hand shanty.

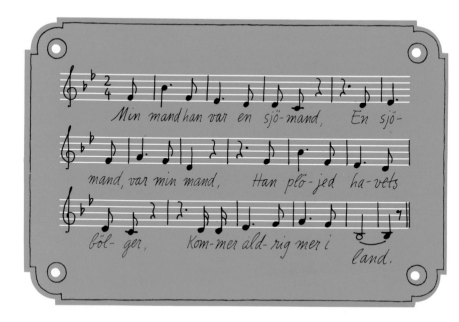

The sad nature of this song, however, hardly fits in with lively hauling. It expresses all the sorrow of a sailor's widow left behind with her five young children, and gives a warning to girls everywhere and for all times — never, never wed a sailor. But in spite of such warnings young girls have seldom been deterred from "setting their caps" for such romantic figures as the bronzed, salt-smelling men-in-blue.

2. Det vaerste som mig grunde,
   När börnene var smaa,
   De ropte: "Kjaere moder,
   Hvor er vaar fader daa?"

3. Han viler ner i graven,
   I graven blot for mig,
   Han kommer ej tilbage,
   Forr än vi smales did.

4. Ja hör nu, piger alle,
   I som vil gifte ger,
   Tag aldrig nogen sjömand,
   Thi sorgen rammer jer.

5. Har nogen lyst at vide,
   Vem visen diktet har?
   Det har en sjömands enke,
   Med sine fem smaa barn.

MY MAN HE WAS A SAILOR

1. My man, he was a seaman,
   A seaman was my man,
   He plowed the sea's billows,
   Will come no more to land.

2. The worst of all it seemed,
   When the children were small,
   They cried, "Our dear mother,
   Where is our father now?"

3. He is resting in the grave,
   In the cold grave before me,
   He will not come back again,
   Before we gather there.

4. Yes, listen all ye lassies,
   You who married wish to be,
   Oh, never wed with a sailor,
   For sorrow you will see.

5. Does anyone wish to know,
   Who has written this lament,
   It is from a sailor's wife,
   Left with her five small babes.

DERRIÈRE CHEZ NOUS

FRENCH: HALYARD SHANTY

The two French publications in which the original words, as sung by the *matelot*, can be found are *Chansons de la Voile "sans Voiles"* and *Cahier de Chansons de Jean Louis Postollec et de Jean La Pipe*. There is a French-Canadian folksong which tells a somewhat similar tale and there is a French folksong too, which starts off: *"Derrière chez nous..."* indicating that Jean Matelot also had a penchant for making his own country's folksongs into shanties, as did other sailormen throughout the world.

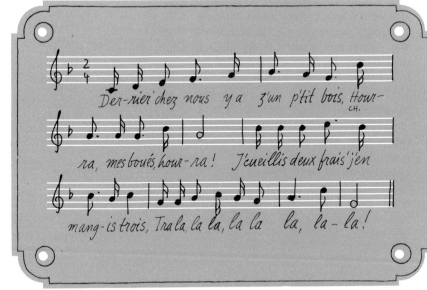

Der-rier chez nous y a z'un p'tit bois, Hour-
ra, mes boués, hour-ra! J'cueillis deux frais'j'en
mang-is trois, Tra la, la la, la la la, la-la!

2. *Avec une fillett' de quinze ans,*
   Sa mère arrive au même instant.

3. *Que faites-vous à mon enfant?*
   J'suis en train d'lui compter les dents.

4. *Il lui en manqu'une sur le d'vant.*

5. *Que je lui pose bellement.*

6. *Il m'en manqu' une également!*

7. *Donnez-moi z'en, marin galant,*

8. *J'les pose qu'à celles de quinze ans.*

9. *Les vieilles pour le commandant!*

The words and phrases in this common hauling song of the French *matelot* seem a little peculiar – the reason being of course, that this is a bowdlerized version (by Captain Hayet) of the original bawdy song, in which there is far more sense.

BACK OF OUR HOUSE

1. At the back of our house there's a little wood,
   Ch.: Hurra, me boys, hurra!
   I gather two strawberries, and I eat three.
   Ch.: Tra la, la la, la la la, la la!

2. Along with a maiden of sweet fifteen,
   Just at that moment her Ma arrives.

3. What are you doing to my little girl?
   I'm in the process of counting her teeth.

4. And she is short one in front.
   (Repeat)

5. So I'm fixing her nicely with a new one.
   (Repeat)

6. I likewise have one missing, too!
   (Repeat)

7. Give me one, bold sailor, do.
   (Repeat)

8. I give them only to young maidens.
   (Repeat)

9. The old ones are for the captain!
   (Repeat)

EN SJÖMAN ÄLSKAR HAVETS VÄG

SWEDISH: CAPSTAN SONG

This shanty probably originated among the seamen of Gävle, Sweden, sometime in the 1870s. Our version was "sung and written down aboard the barque *Chili* from Gävle in 1888 by a deckhand Harold Sundholm," according to A.B. Sodergren, as quoted in *Sång Under Segel*. According to a correspondent in *Svenska Dagbladet* (20 May 1934), the song was composed by a young sea captain, Ossian Limburg, sometime around 1870. I have been informed that it was still being sung aboard Erikson's fleet of Finn sailing ships in the 1930s, but not as a work song.

2. Jag avsked tar av vännen kär, vid vågornas brus,
   Den hulda då mig trohet svär, i stormarnas sus,

3. Hon trycker då så ömt min hand, vid vågornas brus,
   Då känns det tungt att gå från land, till stormarnas sus

4. Hon viskar ömt och ljuvt mitt namn, vid vågornas brus
   "Kom snart tillbaka i min famn, från stormarnas sus!"

5. Min trogna flicka varma kyss – hör vågornas brus,
   För sista gången fick jag nyss, vid stormarnas sus,

6. Där står hon än på stranden grön, vid vågornas brus,
   Och ber till Gud för mig en bön, ur stormarnas sus.

A SAILOR LOVES THE OCEAN WAVES

1. A sailor loves the ocean waves – yes, the roar of the waves,
   When the storm shakes rigging and mast; hear the moan of the storm
   Ch.: Farewell, farewell, fascinating maid, we shall soon return again.

2. I take farewell of my dear friend, by the roar of the waves,
   The dear one then swears to be true, in the moan of the storm.

3. Tenderly she presses my hand, by the roar of the waves,
   Then it feels hard to leave the land, to the moan of the storm.

4. She whispers tenderly my name, by the roar of the waves,
   "Come back soon into my arms, from the moan of the storm."

5. My faithful true love's warm kiss – hear the roar of the waves –
   For the last time I had just now, by the moan of the storm.

6. There she still stands on the green shore, by the roar of the waves,
   And prays to God to keep me safe, from the moan of the storm.

BALLASTLIEDJE

Dutch: Ballast-throwing Shanty

At one time this song had many more verses, now apparently lost. It was a favorite with the fishing inhabitants of the island of Terschelling, as well as those of other Frisian Islands, both seamen and ballast workers. The ballast was taken in baskets from the tidal flats at low tide. It was hoisted aboard the ship by the ship's yardarm, while other workers stowed it in the hold.

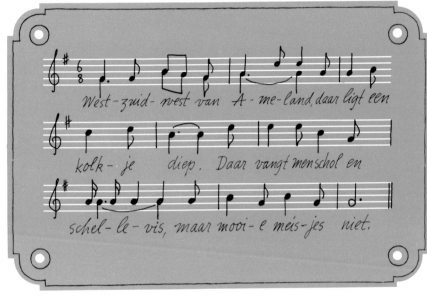

West-zuid-west van A-me-land, daar ligt een kolk-je diep. Daar vangt menschol en schel-le-vis, maar mooi-e meis-jes niet.

2. Hoog zuid hoog van Ameland, de ballast die ligt droog,
   Maar onder op de grond ja grond, is hij zo nat als stront.

3. Hoog is de zolder, laag is de vloer,
   Mooi is 't meisje, maar lelijk is d'r moer.

4. Toen 'k laatst van Suriname kwam, zag ik van ver een schip,
   Ik ducht, dat 't aan de wolken hing, maar het zat op een klip.

5. En op die klip daar zat een koe, een wonderbare koe,
   Die alle maanden kalven moest, ze was er naar aan toe.

BALLAST SONG

1. West-sou'west of Ameland, there's a pool – deep, yes, deep.
   There they catch plaice and haddock, but no handsome girls.

2. High south high of Ameland, the ballast lays dry,
   But below, on the ground, yes, ground, it is as wet as dung.

3. High is the garret, low is the floor,
   Nice is the girl, but ugly is her mother.

4. When I came last from Surinam, from far I saw a ship;
   I thought that it hung in the clouds, but it sat on a reef.

5. And on that reef there sat a cow, a miracle cow,
   Which calved each month – she was in a plight.

Surinam, to where the sailor returns, is in Dutch Guiana on the coast of South America. Along with Curaçao and Aruba, it was an important port-o'-call, in the old days, for Dutch West Indiamen. Timbers such as guaiacum (lignum vitae) and greenheart were common hardwood cargoes from the Guianas; the guaiacum was used to make ships' blocks.

QUAND LA BOITEUSE VA-T-AU MARCHÉ

FRENCH: CAPSTAN SHANTY

The translation of this shanty is not so bold as in the original French. Here again is the typical Gallic way of repeating the solos of their shanties as refrains. The word *mousse* refers to a deck-boy or ship's boy. Variations of that word are found throughout the fo'c'sles of continental ships. In German ships the word used is "Moses"; if there were more than one deck-boy the eldest would be called *Laufer Messe*. Norwegians used the word "Moses," although a first-tripper was often called, ironically, *båsen* (bosun). A first-tripper boy in French *long-courriers* (deepwatermen) usually slept aft, had his meals in the pantry, and was called a *mousse de chambre*. When he became sixteen he was called a *novice* and moved into the fo'c'sle.

2. *Elle emmène aussi son gabier,*
   C'est lui qui fait manoeuvrier.

3. *Sur fond de plumes la fait mouiller,*
   Lui prend trois ris dans son tablier.

4. *Et sa cotte lui fait carguer,*
   Sa chemise lui fait serrer.

5. *Puis à courir le beau gabier,*
   Il lui guinde un mât de hunier.

6. *Quand la boiteuse vient du marché,*
   Qu'apporte-t-elle dans son panier?

7. *Un petit mousse sur chantier,*
   Avec dix mois sera lancé.

WHEN THE LAME ONE GOES TO MARKET

1. When the lame one goes to market,
   Ch.: When the lame one goes to market!
   With her nice little basket,
   Ch.: With her nice little basket,
       Away she goes hobbling,
       Oh, Mama, do not cry so much!
   Full ch.: Oh, my dear, what treasure,
       To have married, to have wed,
       Oh, my dear, what treasure,
       To have married, to have wed,
       A heart of gold!

2. She brings with her, her sailor,
   It is he who guides her along.

3. On a feather-bed he makes her anchor,
   And takes three reefs in her apron.

4. And then he furls her petticoat,
   Clewing up her lower sails.

5. Then to get goin' the smart topman,
   Sends up the main topmast.

6. When the lame one comes from market,
   What does she carry in her basket?

7. A little deck-boy already on the stocks,
   Launched before ten months are out.

WHALERS, FISHERMEN, SMUGGLERS AND PIRATES

The hardy men who manned the sailing whalers were a species entirely apart from the deep-water sailor. On account of the nature of their calling, sailors as such – men who steered, handled her sails, and maintained her gear – were in the minority. Small boat handlers (which many deep-water seamen were not) were always in demand in whalers. Coopers were also needed; their job was to make the "knocked-down" staves into barrels when the whaling grounds were reached. The harpooners, too, were a class apart from normal seamen. Their chief was called, from the Dutch, a "Speckshoneer." Then there were the general dogbodies who flensed (stripped) the blubber,

kept the trypots a-boiling, and so on, as well as cooks and stewards – the "shipkeepers," who stayed aboard the main vessel when everyone else was out a-hunting. Although the whale is a mammal, whalers always referred to them as "fish" and their business as "fishing." Of true fishing the toughest must have been that of the Newfoundland cod fishermen. It was so tough that the French penal system used the *terre neuvas* of the Breton cod-fleet as alternatives to sending a criminal to Devil's Island. The most spectacular of all the fishing trades, I fancy, is that of the tuna fisherman of the island of Sicily. At certain seasons the tuna are driven toward long nets, like corridors, which eventually lead to a large rectangular net – "the death chamber." Around the upper edge of this "chamber" hundreds of small boats are clustered. As the great "death chamber" is hauled up to the wild cries and songs of excited fishermen, the tuna find themselves in less and less water and begin to throw themselves madly about. When the net is almost out of the water the *matanza* or "kill" commences, the great trapped tuna thrashing about as the fishermen give each its death blow.

Smuggling and wrecking, in days gone by, went hand in hand. Smuggling needs little explaining here but it is worth remarking on the cruel, if romantic, game of wrecking. Around the Cornish coasts when a ship was to be wrecked, the wreckers would tie a lantern between the horns of a hobbled cow – "jibber the kibber," it was called – such a lantern giving the crew of the unsuspecting ship the idea that it marked

the entrance to the port. As soon as the ship struck the rocks, the wreckers would be on the spot, killing and looting.

Pirates, of course, belonged to no country, but were of all countries. The buccaneers of the West Indies, who were originally French cattle-raisers, took their name from the Carib method of cooking meat, on a *boucan*. It was only when the Spaniards made life difficult on Haiti that these men took to piracy and were joined by the outcasts of all nations. Of well-known pirates here are a few names that have come down from the past: the Frenchmen, Pierre le Grand, Misson, and l'Olonnois; the Dutchmen, Mansveld, Rock Brasiliano, and Esquemeling; the Welshmen, Morgan and Howell Davies; the Portuguese, Bartolomeu; the Englishmen, Kidd, Teach (Blackbeard), Bonnet, and Avery, and the greatest of the Barbary Corsairs – Barbarossa.

BRINDISI DI MARINAI

SICILIAN/ITALIAN:
WORK SONG, for hauling the nets

This is another work song used by the fishermen of the Trapani province of Sicily when raising the tuna nets. A few of these tuna fishermen's net-hauling songs have been collected for us through the efforts of the folksong collectors Alan Lomax, of America, and Diego Carpitella, of Italy. In many cases, although given as hauling songs, they were sung at the capstan. In the larger boats, the trawl lines were taken to the capstan and the nets heaved in, rather than being hauled in by hand, and the men sang while pushing at the bars.

A SAILOR TOAST

We must put out the lamp, boys!
From here we'll not be moving!
This lamp it must be doused, boys!
For we all feel like drinking.
We want to mix the drinks, boys!
For here we'll all be staying!
From here we'll not be moving!
We must put out the lamp, boys!
We'll drink a bully toast, boys,
To the one who gives employment.
And we must all be drinking,
Our biscuits we'll be soaking.

All hands: Bacchus! Bacchus!

ALLEN DIE VILLEN NAAR ISLAND

DUTCH: FOREBITTER

This is a song of the codfishers of Iceland. My source for the song, Kees Hos, told me that he had found the place-names as given in the song on an old Dutch sea-chart. They are as follows: *Lezart*, the Lizard; *Sorlines*, the Scillies; and *Kaap Clara*, Cape Clear. Rockall was the same as in the song, *Rokol*. *Kollen*, in the sixth verse, is Old Dutch for the type of cod-lines with hooks used on the Iceland Ground. Both the Dutch and the Breton cod-fishermen were once great frequenters of the grounds off Iceland.

Al-len, die wil-len naar Ise-land gaan, Om ka-bel-jauw te van-gen, En te vis-sen met ver-lan-gen, Naar I-se-land, naar I-se-land, naar Ise-land toe, Tot drie en der-tig rei-zen zijn wij nog niet moe.

2. Komt ons de tijd van de fooie aan,
Wij dansen met behagen,
En wij weten van geen klagen,
Maar komt de tijd, maar komt de tijd, naar zee te gaan,
Dan is er wel ans hoofd van zorgen zwaar belaan.

3. Als er de wind van het Noorden waait,
Wij gaan naar de herberge,
En wij drinken zonder erge;
Wij drinken daar, wij drinken daar, op ons gemak,
Tordat de leste stuiver is uit onze zak.

4. Als er de wind van 't Oosten waait,
De schipper blij van herte,
Zegt: "Die wind, die speelt ons perten,
'T zal beter zijn, 't zal beter zijn, 't zal beter zijn,
Te lopen voor de wind recht het Kanaal maar in."

5. "Langs de Lezaars, de Schorels voorbij,
Van daar al naar Kaap Claire,
Die niet weet hij zal 't wel leren."
Toen komt er bij, toen komt er bij, ons stureman,
En hij geeft ons de koerse recht naar Iseland.

6. Wij lopen 't eiland Rokol voobij,
Al naar de vogelscharen,
Dat zal ieder openharen,
En dan vandaar, en dan vandaar, naar Bredefjord,
En daar dan smijten wij de kollen buiten boord.

7. Eind'lijk dan komen w'op Iseland aan,
Om kabeljauw te vangen,
En te vissen met verlangen,
Naar Iseland, naar Iseland, naar Iseland toe,
Tot drie en dertig reizen zijn wij nog niet moe.

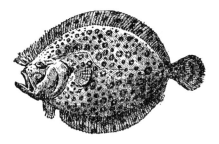

ALL WHO WANT TO ICELAND GO

1. All who want to Iceland go,
   For the catching of the cod,
   And to fish with desire,
   To Iceland, to Iceland, to Iceland,
   Thirty-three voyages and we're not yet weary.

2. When the time comes for us to be paid,
   We dance with happiness,
   None of us complaining,
   But when we have to go to sea, go to sea,
   Then is our head heavy with care.

3. When the wind blows from the north,
   We go to the inn,
   And we drink without thinking,
   There we drink at our ease,
   Till the last coin is spent.

4. When the wind blows from the east,
   The skipper's glad in his heart,
   Saying, "That wind it plays us tricks,
   It will be better, it will be better,
   To sail before the wind through the Channel."

5. "Pass the Lizard and the Scillies beyond,
   From there to Cape Clear,
   If you don't know the route you will soon learn.
   Then comes the mate, comes the mate,
   Giving us the course straight to Iceland.

6. We'll pass the isle of Rockall,
   From the great crowds of birds,
   It will be clear where we are,
   And onward, onward to Breidifjord.
   Where we'll put the lines out.

7. At last we arrive in Iceland,
   Ready to catch cod,
   And to fish with pleasure,
   To Iceland, to Iceland,
   Thirty-three trips and we're still not tired.

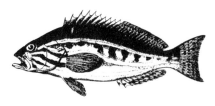

E AMÒLA

SICILIAN: FISHERMAN'S WORK SONG

This is a work song used by the tunny fishermen of Western Sicily. The invoking of patron saints – the Virgin Mary and St. Giuseppe – to help the fisherman in his chore occurs all around the coasts of Sicily and Italy in general. Fishermen call on their patron saints to aid them in their work and to ward off all evil and preserve them from the dangers of the sea and from the rigors of their lives.

E-mu-nin-ni cu' Ma-ri-a! E a-mò-la e a-mò-la! San Giu-sep-pe'n cum-pa-gnia! E a-mò-la e à- mò-la!

2. E lu tunnu è veru beddu!
   Carricamu 'stu vasceddu!

3. E di Genuva a Portufinu,
   E Livurnu signurinu.

4. E assummamu 'sta safina!
   E sparamu 'sta tunnina!

   All hands: Assumma!
              Assumma!

1. Let us begin to work,
   In the company of the Virgin and St. Giuseppe

2. The tunny are abundant,
   Let us load up our ship.

3. We will go to the lordly cities,
   Of Genoa, Portofino, and Leghorn.

4. We'll raise the nets of the tunny,
   And make the fish disappear.

   All hands: Up with the net! Up with the net!

Fishermen from Genoa place their trust in Madonna della Coronata, those from the Riviera di Levante in the Madonna di Montellegro (at Rapallo). The fishermen of Naples swear to the aid given by the Madonna di Piedigrotta. Tuscan fishermen and mariners (and steamboat firemen, too) have always revered the Madonna di Montenero of Leghorn, while the seamen of Ancona and Rimini believe strongly in the powers of Our Lady of Morato. And the seafarers of the Adriatic have San Nicola of Bari as their protector.

FISCHERLIED

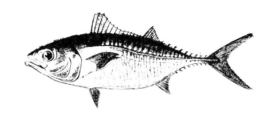

GERMAN: FOREBITTER

This is a fisherman's song from the coast of Pomerania *(Pommersche Küste)*, revealing the thoughts in the mind of a young fisherman as he hauls his nets in the waters of the Baltic Sea — thoughts of his sweetheart and of his coming marriage.

Ein ar-mer Fi- scher bin ich zwar, ver-dien'mein
Geld stets in Ge- fahr, Doch wenn Feins- lieb-
chen am U-fer ruht, dann geht das Fi- schen
noch ein-mal so gut. Doch wenn Feins- gut.

2. Und fahren wir zur See hinaus, und werfen
   uns're Netze aus.
   Dann kommen Fischlein gross und klein, ein jedes
   will einmal gefangen sein.

3. Und ist vorbei der Monat Mai, vorbei ist dann
   die Fischerei,
   Dann geht Feinsliebchen zum Traualtar, es lebe
   hoch das Fischerpaar.

FISHERMAN'S SONG

1. I'm a poor fisherman who earns his money dangerously,
   But when my sweetheart is on the strand, then, feeling good, I go about my job.
   (Repeat last line in each verse as chorus)

2. And off we go to sea and cast the nets o'erside,
   The fishes come – big and small, and we make 'em captive every one.

3. And when the month of May has passed, 'tis then the fishing'll be over,
   And I will splice my lovely sweetheart, life is fine for a fishing couple.

ROLLING DOWN TO OLD MAUI

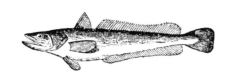

AMERICAN/ENGLISH: FOREBITTER

The Hawaiian island of Maui, or Mowhee as it is written in the old manuals, was a popular headquarters and wintering port of the sperm and bowhead whalemen from the early days of the nineteenth century onward. The small port of Lahaina was, in 1820, the capital of the Sandwich Islands, as the Hawaiian group was then named. Situated as it is with the island of Lanai to the west'ard and that of Kahoolawe to the south'ard, the town has a magnificent bay and possesses a fine anchorage. During the year 1846, 395 sailing ships, mainly whalers, dropped anchor there.

The whalemen worked two seasons – the "large," when the fleet went north to the Sea of Okhotsk after the bowhead whale, and the "small," when they cruised off the coast of Baja, California, after the California grey whale. After being away in the icy Okhotsk Sea, a period of hard work, ice, no booze, and no girls, the whalemen would arrive back in Lahaina all ready to tear the town apart. It didn't take long for sailors to desert here and many set up grog-shops, the focal point of the visiting whalemen. The so-called Ship Girls, or native *wahines*, would swim out to the incoming whale fleet. Although it was taboo for a female to enter a canoe, they would climb up the chain-plates and bobstays with agility, and in no time each ship became a scene of wild boozing and orgies. In later years Honolulu took over from Lahaina as the main port and the whalemen didn't "roll down to old Maui" any more.

'Tis a rough, tough life of toil an' strife, we whale-men un-der go, We don't give a damn when the gale is done, how hard the winds do blow; We're home-ward bound, 'tis a damn fine sound, with a good ship taut an' free - - -, We don't give a damn when we drink our rum, with the girls of old Mau-ee. Roll-ing down to old Mau-ee, me boys, Roll-ing down to old Mau-ee - - -ee, We're home-ward bound from the Arc-tic ground Rolling down to old Mau-ee!

2. Once more we sail with a northerly gale through the ice an' sleet an' rain,
   And them coconut fronds in them tropic lands, oh, we soon shall see again,
   Six hellish months have passed away in the cold Kamchatka Sea,
   But now we're bound from the Arctic ground, rolling down to old Maui!

   3. We'll heave the lead where old Diamond Head looms up on ol' Wahoo,
      Our masts and yards are sheathed with ice, an' our decks are hid from view,
      The horrid ice of the sea-cut tiles that deck the Arctic Sea,
      Are miles behind in the frozen wind since we steered for old Maui.

4. How soft the breeze of the tropic seas now the ice is far astern,
   And them native maids in them island glades are awaiting our return,
   An' their big black eyes even now look out, hoping some fine day to see,
   Our baggy sails running 'fore the gales, rolling down to old Maui.

   5. An' now we sail with a favorable gale toward our island home,
      Our mainyard sprung, all whaling done, an' we ain't got far to roam;
      Our stuns'l booms are carried away, what care we for that sound?
      A livin' gale is arter us, thank God we're homeward bound.

6. And now we're anchored in the Bay with the Kanakas all around,
   With chants and soft aloha oes they greet us homeward bound;
   An' now ashore we'll have good fun, we'll paint them beaches red,
   Awakin' in the arms of an island maid, with a big, fat, achin' head.

THE FEMALE SMUGGLER

ENGLISH: FOREBITTER

Smuggling was the usual way of life on the Channel coast of England during the sixteenth, seventeenth, and eighteenth centuries, performed by all manner of citizens from criminal to the clergy. Smuggling and its counterpart, wrecking, were the natural livelihoods of the peasants and fishermen of Cornwall in particular. French brandy, silks and brocades, tobacco, not to mention human beings in the form of spies and infiltrators, crossed the Channel hourly. The customs or preventive officers are referred to in this song as the "Blockade." As described here, smugglers and pirates were often at "loggerheads." As Captain Whall points out, this type of sailor-song was sung with a "d" sound coming before emphasized "l"s and "n"s; e.g., a-whidle (awhile), rodling (rolling), shadll (shall), adnd (and), and soodn (soon).

O come, list a-while, and ye soon shall hear,
By the roll-in' sea lived a mai-den fair,
Her fath-er fol-lowed the smugg-ling trade, Like a war-like he-ro,
Like a war-like he-ro, that nev-er was a-fraid.

2. Now, in sailor's clothing young Jane did go,
   Dressed like a sailor from tip to toe,
   Her aged father was the only care,
   Of this female smuggler,
       Of this female smuggler, who never did despair.

3. With her pistols loaded she went aboard,
   And by her side hung a glittering sword,
   In her belt two daggers - well armed for war,
   Was this female smuggler,
       Was this female smuggler, who never feared a scar.

4. Now they had not sailed far from land,
   When a strange sail brought them to a stand,
   "These are sea robbers," this maid did cry,
   "But the female smuggler,
       But the female smuggler, will conquer or die."

5. Alongside, then, this strange vessel came,
   "Cheer up," cried Jane, "we will board the same;
   We'll run all chances to rise or fall,"
   Cried this female smuggler,
       Cried this female smuggler, who never feared a ball.

6. Now they killed those pirates and took their store,
   An' soon returned to ol' Eng-a-land's shore,
   With a keg of brandy she walked along,
   Did this female smuggler,
       Did this female smuggler, and sweetly sang a song.

7. Now they were followed by the Blockade,
   Who in irons strong did put this fair maid,
   But when they brought her for to be tried,
   This young female smuggler,
       This young female smuggler, stood dressed like a bride.

8. The commander to the judge then said,
   "I cannot prosecute this maid,
   Pardon for her on my knees I crave,
   For this female smuggler,
       For this female smuggler, so valiant and so brave."

9. Then the commander to her father went,
   To gain her hand he asked consent,
   His consent he gained, so the commander,
   And the female smuggler,
       And the female smuggler, are a happy pair.

123

DUNDEE WHALERS

SCOTTISH: FOREBITTER

This is a genuine whalers' song which found its way into the fo'c'sles of British merchant ships. The Canadians also have a version sung to a different tune.

It is possible that Othere, the Norwegian, was the first to make a voyage beyond the North Cape in search of whales, but these were "horse-whales" or walrus. He brought back their tusks for King Alfred of England. The Dutch, however, were the first to establish a whaling station at Spitzbergen in the Arctic Ocean, although the Basques whaled in the Bay of Biscay earlier still. Spitzbergen was always referred to as East Greenland, and many early whaling songs about Greenland may in fact be about Spitzbergen.

Histories of the ships mentioned in this song, with the exception of *Erin's Boy*, can be found in Basil Lubbock's fine book *The Arctic Whalers* (reprint 1968). I learned this song from an old Dundee (Scotland) whalerman who told me that when heaving up the anchor in Dundee whalers it was often played by a piper (most Scottish whalers had a piper aboard).

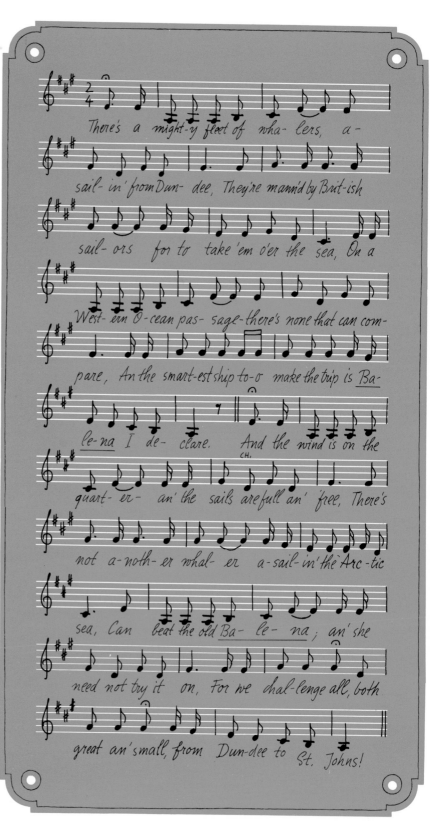

There's a might-y fleet of wha-lers, a-sail-in' from Dun-dee, They're mann'd by Brit-ish sail-ors for to take 'em o'er the sea, On a West-ern O-cean pas-sage-there's none that can com-pare, An the smart-est ship to-o make the trip is Ba-le-na I de-clare. And the wind is on the quart-er- an' the sails are full an' free, There's not a-noth-er whal-er a-sail-in' the Arc-tic sea, Can beat the old Ba-le-na; an' she need not try it on, For we chal-lenge all, both great an' small, from Dun-dee to St. Johns!

2. There's the new-built Terra Nova, she's a model without doubt,
   The Arctic and Aurora, ye've heard so much about;
   There's Jackson's model mail boat, the terror of the sea,
   But she couldn't beat Balena on the passage from Dundee.

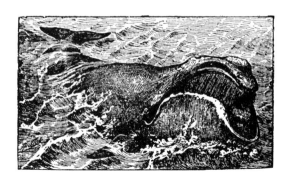

3. Bold Jackson carries canvas an' fairly raises steam,
   An' Capen Gay with the Erin Boy goes plowin' thro' the stream,
   An' Mullen says the Eskimeaux will beat the bloomin' lot,
   To beat the ol' Balena, oh, she'll find it rather hot.

4. An' now that we are landed where the rum is mighty cheap,
   We'll drink success to our capen for guidin' us o'er the deep,
   A health to all our sweethearts an' to our wives so fair,
   Not another ship could make that trip but Balena I declare.

REUBEN RANZO

AMERICAN/ENGLISH:
HALYARD SHANTY

A theory of mine on the origin of this shanty is given in the notes on "Brindisi di Marinai." "Reuben Ranzo" was a shanty popular with the sailor because it gave him the opportunity for sly innuendoes directed aft at the officers. This song, of course, is the story of a greenhorn sailor who, although no good at practical seamanship, manages to acquire enough of its sister but gentler art, navigation, to become the captain of a whaler.

Although it is doubtful whether hauling shanties were used to any extent aboard whalers (their big crews obviating the need of them), it has always been thought that this song was indeed sung aboard whalers, but not for hauling. Windlass songs were used aboard the blubber-hunters when hauling the blubber to the masthead and for other daily chores; and of course whalers sang, and were the originators of, many forebitters.

The tune varies only slightly in all the collected versions, and the only difference in the text is in the final stanzas:

1. He is thrown overboard for his dirty habits.
2. He is lashed for stealing the captain's turkey.
3. He has further adventures at the bottom of the sea after being thrown overboard.

In a long hoist the shantyman would repeat the solo lines. The pulls came on the two "Ranzo"s in both refrains. The Swedes and Norwegians too had their own language versions of this shanty.

2. Ranzo wuz no sailor,
   He shipped aboard a whaler.

3. Ranzo joined Pierre Loti,
   Did not know his dooty.

4. Shanghaied aboard of a whaler,
   They tried to make him a sailor.

5. They put him holystoning,
   And cared not for his groaning.

6. They gave him lashes thirty,
   Because he wuz so dirty.

7. He washed once in a fortnight,
   Said it wuz his birthright.

8. The cap'n gave him thirty,
   His daughter begged for mercy.

9. She gave him soap an' water,
   An' a bit more than she oughter.

10. She gave him rum and whiskey,
    Which made him feel damned frisky.

11. She taught him navigation,
    An' gave him edication.

12. She made him the best sailor,
    Sailing on that whaler.

13. Ranzo's now the skipper,
    Of a Yankee whaler.

126

ET NOUS IRONS À VALPARAISO

FRENCH: CAPSTAN SHANTY

If one listens closely to the air of this song it will be noted instantly that the first half is the tune of the English shanty "Goodbye-fare-ye-well" and the second half that of "Blow the Man Down." Originally sung, according to H. Jacques, by *les baleiniers des mers du Sud* (whalers of the South Seas), as its whaling content implies, in later years it became the property of the French Cape-Horners engaged in the Chilean saltpeter trade. It would be the shanty used aboard the ships of the famous Gallic sailing-ship companies, when they were heaving up their anchors for the last time, homeward bound from the Flaming Coast of Chile, scupper deep with saltpeter, nitrate, and guano. The verses here have been bowdlerized a little by Captain Hayet. The third refrain would be given a "hitch" on the *oula* by an experienced crowd of sailormen.

2. Plus d'un y laissera sa peau,
   Adieu misère, adieu bateau!
   Et nous irons à Valparaiso,
   Où d'autres laisseront leurs os.

3. Ceux qui r'viendront pavillon haut,
   C'est premier brin de matelot,
   Pour la bordée ils seront à flot,
   Bon pour le rack, la fille, le couteau.

BOUND FOR VALPARAISO

1. Hurrah, me bullies, heave the capstan O!
   Ch.: Goodbye fa-re-well, goodbye fa-re-well!
   Hurrah, me bullies, farewell Bordeaux!
   Ch.: Hourra, O Mexico!
   At Cape Horn it won't be so hot,
   Ch.: Haul away-hé! Oula tchalez!
   Fishing, me boys, for big cachalot.
   Ch.: Haul away, John, oh, haul away O!

2. More than one will lose his hide.
   Goodbye to the drudgery, goodbye to the ship.
   Then we'll be bound for Valparaiso,
   Where others of us will leave our bones.

3. But those who return with the flags flying high,
   Each sure will be one hell of a guy.
   For a spree ashore they'll always be ripe,
   Just the chaps for the rum, the gals, or the knife!

127

PIQUE LA BALEINE

FRENCH: ROWING SHANTY

This is one of the few rowing songs (*chanson à ramer*) to have survived in France, a country where the rowing of galleys lasted into the beginning of the nineteenth century. In other countries such songs are even more difficult to find. This is a whalers' song used by the French South Seas sperm-whaler-men when, after having sighted their quarry, the boats were lowered and the oarsmen moved, long and deep, in their efforts to approach ("wood and black skin") the huge leviathan. Then the harpooner (*balancier*) would strike with his harpoon, hoping to get a secure hold.

Pour re-trou-ver ma douce a-mie, oh, mes boués! Ouh! la ouh! la, la, la! Pi-que la ba-lei-ne, jo-li ba-lei-nier, Pi-que la ba-lei-ne, je veux na-vi-guer!

2. Aux mille mers j'ai navigué, oh, mes boués!

3. Des mers du Nord aux mers du Sud, oh, mes boués!

4. Je l'ai r'trouvée quand j'm'ai noyé, oh, mes boués!

5. Dans les grands fonds elle m'espérait, oh, mes boués!

6. En couple à elle me suis couché, oh, mes boués!

STRIKE THE WHALE

1. For to find my love again, oh, me boys!
   Ch.: Oh, la, oh! la, la, la!
   Strike the whale, lovely harpooner,
   Strike the whale, I willingly sail!

2. To a thousand seas I sail, oh, me boys!

3. The seas of the North and of the South, oh, me boys!

4. I'll find my love even if she's drowned, oh, me boys!

5. I'll find her awaiting me in the great deeps, oh, me boys!

6. Embraced with her will be my bed, oh, me boys!

Once the harpoon was well into the great bulk, oars were tossed and, with the whale-line pulled taut like a bow-string, the whale would race away at twenty knots, giving the rowers what they called a "Nantucket sleigh ride." When the monster weakened, the boats would again approach and the boatsteerer would carefully place the lance into the poor beast's heart, causing it to burst and his "chimney to go afire," when his blowhole would spout blood. The theme of our song, that of a lover looking for a drowned love, is one similar to that found in the English windlass song, "Lowlands."

128

EIGHT BELLS

ENGLISH: FOREBITTER

This forebitter was well known in the 1880s aboard British ships and in particular aboard whalers. However, it is not associated with the Arctic whalers of Dundee, Hull, Peterhead, and so on, but rather more with the sperm-fishermen of the South Seas, for it tells about a seaman being "in the hoops."

Oh, me hus-band's a sau-cy fore to-op man, Oh, a chum of the cook, don't ye kno-ow! He put his head down the cook's fu-un-nel, An' he shout-ed come up from be-low. Eight bells, eight bells— Rouse out there the watch from be-low. Eight bells, eight bells— Rouse out there the watch from be-low!

Now, in all Arctic whalers, the look-out's position was, for protection from the cold, inside a barrel at the mast-head. In warmer regions of the South Pacific the barrel was not required. Most South Seas seamen had another set of crosstrees above the normal top-mast crosstrees, part way up the t'gal-lant mast. Above these again, secured to the royal mast, were two hoops, in which the lookout stood with his feet on the t'gallant crosstrees. Whaleships, when "fishing," rarely set royals; in fact nothing was set above the t'gal-lants except when homeward bound, when every kite would be spread aloft including stuns'ls.

2. My husband once shipped in a whaler,
   An' he sailed to the far northern seas,
   An' bein' a bold-hearted sailor,
   He cared not for ice, sea, nor breeze.

3. When up in the hoops he wuz dandy,
   At sightin' a whale when she blows,
   When out in a whaleboat wuz handy,
   A smarter young tar never rowed.

4. At the end of his watch, oh, his fancy,
   Wuz to git to his bunk quickly O!
   For he wanted to dream o' his Nancy,
   So he shouted "Come up from below!"

5. An' now he's no longer a sailor,
   He often wakes up in the night,
   Thinkin' he's still on that whaler,
   Shouts out wi' the greatest delight.

129

FISH OF THE SEA

ENGLISH/AMERICAN: FOREBITTER,
also used at Capstan and Pumps

The best-known version of this song is the one sung in the thirties by the famous Scottish contralto, Katherine Ferrier – "Blaw the Wind Southerly." The River Tyne area of northern England also claims an early version. However, the song moved rapidly across the world, and the Gloucester fishermen of the northeast coast of America soon had their own variant. A faster and musically more complicated number comes from the fishermen of Newfoundland and Nova Scotia. England has another variant found in the Bristol Channel ports, but the one we give here probably hailed from the southeast of England.

I'll sing ye a song of the fish of the sea, An' I'll trust that ye'll join in this cho-rus wi' me, Wi' a wind-y ol' weath-er! Storm-y ol' weath-er! When the wind blows, we'll all heave to-geth-er!

Although seemingly the property of fishermen, the song was soon popular in the fo'c'sles of British sailing ships, where it was sometimes used at the capstan or pumps. In the fo'c'sle it was often sung with the men sitting in a circle on their sea-chests or wooden benches. The group would appoint a leader, whose job it was to see that each man sang a verse connected with a certain fish. With a good singing crowd that could improvise, the song might go on for hours.

2. There wuz once an ol' skipper, I don't know his name,
   But I know that he once played a bloomin' fine game.

3. When his ship lay becalmed in a tropical sea,
   He whistled all day, but in vain, for a breeze.

4. But a seal heard his whistle an' loudly did call,
   "Just stow your light canvas, jib, spanker, an' all."

5. "I'll send ye some fish to consult if you please,
   The best way to git ye a nice whistling breeze."

6. Oh, first came the herring sayin', "I'm king o' the sea,"
   He jumped on the poop, "Oh, the cap'n I'll be!"

7. Next came the shark with his two rows o' teeth,
   Sayin', "Ye mind the cabbage an' I'll mind the beef."

8. Next came the codfish with his chuckle head,
   He jumped in the chains an' began heavin' the lead.

9. Next came the mackerel wid his pretty striped back,
   He hauled aft each sheet an' he boarded each tack.

10. Then came the sprat, the smallest of all,
    He jumped on the poop an' cried, "Maintops'l haul!"

11. The breeze it blew gaily an' gaily sailed he,
    But what an ol' rascal that skipper must be.

STÖRTEBEKER

Störtebeker was a famous German pirate of the fourteenth century who, along with Godekins (Godeke) and Moltke and Menteufel (known as the Vitalian Brothers), formed a league called "The Friends of God and Enemies of the World." These four caused havoc around the North Sea, Baltic Sea, and English Channel. When the Swedes and Danes were at war, the pirates kept Stockholm supplied with food from their headquarters on Gotland. The Hanseatic League decided to end their multifarious careers and sent Simon of Utrecht along with a fleet of Hanseatic cogs to curtail their machinations. The four, along with seventy of their shipmates, were executed in Hamburg in 1402. All were beheaded.

2. De Störtebeker reep: "All' to Hand,
   De Westsee is uns woll bekannt,
   Darhenn wüllt wi nu faren,
   De riken Kooplüüd von Hamborg,
   Moten jemmer Scheep nu waaren."

3. Nu lepen se wi dull darhenn,
   In eren bösen Röversinn.
   Bet dat man jem kreeg faten,
   Bi't Hillgeland in aller Frö,
   Dar mussen se dat Haat wull laten.

4. De Bunte Ko ut Flandern kaam,
   Dat Rov-Schipp up de Hoten naam,
   Un stött et wiss in Stücken.
   Dat Dolk se brochten na Hamborg rop,
   Dar mussen se den Kopp all missen.

5. De Drone de heet Rosenfeld,
   Haut af so manken willen Held,
   Den Kopp mit köölem Mode,
   He hatte angesnoorte Schoh,
   Bet an sien Enkel stunn he in Bloote.

1. Störtebeker and Micheel, allies in piracy,
   Shared their prey equally ashore and at sea,
   But God was offended by their terrible deeds,
   And shame was the end of their fruitless seeds.

2. Klas Störtebeker called "All hands to me!
   Let us sail to the well-known Western Sea!"
   And: "Hamburg merchantmen beware!
   Look out! We come! Take special care!"

3. And there they sailed, grapnels in hand,
   They tempted God, it was their end.
   Near Heligoland in the morning light,
   They met their master in a furious fight.

4. The *Bunte Kutz*'s beak rammed the pirate frigate,
   And this was their end, their shameful fate,
   They were brought to Hamburg, in iron chains,
   Their heads to lose and thus end their strain.

5. Drone Rosenfeld was the hangman's name,
   Many a head under his sword there came,
   He bound his shoes up to their highest point,
   For he stood in blood soon to his ankle-joint.

131

THE FOURTEENTH OF FEBRUARY

ENGLISH: FOREBITTER

This English forebitter is one of fair antiquity, going back to the days when the high seas were riddled with pirates of all nations. There is a distinct folk-process noticed in the geographical names involved. It is very doubtful whether in the original a ship bound for Newfoundland from London would be going via Callao, Peru – a long way round, one would think!

On the fourteenth of February, we-e sailed from the la-and, In the bold Princess Ro-oy-al bound for New-en-foun' land, We had forty-five sea-men--for a ship's comp-an-ee—ee, An' the wind from the ee-east'ard, to the west'ard steered we.

2. We'd hardly been sailin' but a day two or three,
When the man from the masthead, strange sail he did see.
She came bearin' down on us wid her tops'ls so high,
An' under her mizen-peak black colors did fly.

3. An' when this bold pirate he'd hove alongside,
With a loud speakin' voice, "We are comin'!" he cried,
"We come from fair London bound to Callao,
So hinder us not in our passage to go!"

4. "Back yer maintops'l an' heave yer ship to,
For I have a letter to be carried home by you."
"I'll back me main tops'l an' heave me ship to,
But only in some harbor an' alongside o' you!"

5. He chased us to wind'ard throughout the long day,
He chased us to loo'ard but he could not gain way,
An' he fired long-shot arter us, but he could not prevail,
An' the bold Princess Royal soon showed a clean tail.

6. Go down to yer grog, me lads, go down every one,
Go down to yer grog, me lads, go down one an' all,
Go down to yer grog, me lads, an' be of good cheer,
For as long as we've sea-room, we've nothin' to fear.

A song of roughly the same age with a similar theme is that called "High Barbaree." Both these songs stem from the period (1600s–1700s) when the English Channel – "Sea of Sick Heads and Sore Hearts" – and the Narrow Seas were infested with pirates and privateers. These consisted mainly of Bretons, Flemings, Swedes, Irish, and Basques, and even Barbary Corsairs who left their coasts of Sallee and sailed northward to sink ships and sack small ports around the sou'west coasts of Britain. The tune we give here is one of several, but it is interesting to note that it is one that has been given to the words of John Bunyan's hymn "Immortal, Invisible."

LE TRENTE-ET-UN DU MOIS D'AOÛT

FRENCH: FOREBITTER

This song is sometimes called the "Song of the Corsairs" and comes from the days of Louis XVI. The word "corsair" is hardly applicable since the enemy ship in the song is obviously an English privateer of the type who, without waiting for an actual war between England and France, would still nibble at anything she considered non-English. In the three slightly different versions I have come across, the port she hails from or heads back to can be either Glasgow, Breslau, or Bordeaux. *Les perroquets* (parrakeets) is the French sailors' colloquial term for the t'gallant sails; the royals were called *coquetois* (cockatoos).

Le trente et un du mois d'a-oût, Nous vîmes ar-ri-ver sur nous, Une fré-ga-te d'An-gle-terre, Qui ra-sait la mer et les flots, Pour s'en al-ler jusqu'à Bres-lau!

2. Le capitaine, en la voyant,
   Fit appeler son lieutenant,
   "Lieutenant, êtes-vous assez brave,
   Lieutenant, êtes-vous assez fort,
   Pour aller accoster son bord ?"

3. Le lieutenant fier et hardi,
   Lui répondit, "Capitaine, oui !"
   "Faites monter votre équipage,
   Braves soudards et matelots,
   Faites-les tous monter en haut."

4. Le maître donne un coup de sifflet,
   "En haut ! largue les perroquets !
   Largue les ris, et vent arrière,
   Laisse arriver près de son bord,
   Pour voir qui sera le plus fort !"

5. "Vire lof pour lof ! En abattant !"
   Nous l'accostâmes, par son avant ;
   A coups de hâche d'abordage,
   A coups de piques et de mousquetons,
   Nous l'avons mis à la raison.

6. Que dira-t-on de lui tantôt,
   En Angleterre et à Breslau,
   D'avoir laissé prendre sa frégate,
   Par un corsaire de dix canons,
   Qui qu'en avait trent-six et de bons ?

THE THIRTY-FIRST OF AUGUST

1. On the thirty-first of August,
   We saw bearing down on us,
   (Repeat first two lines in each verse)
   An English frigate,
   She raced across the sea and waves,
   Heading for Breslau.
   Ch.: Let us drink once, twice,
       A health to all lovers,
       (Repeat first two lines)
       A health to the king of France,
       Shit on the king of England,
       Who has declared war on us.

2. The captain, when he saw her,
   Called his lieutenant,
   "Lieutenant are you brave enough,
   Are you strong enough,
   To go and board her?"

3. The lieutenant, fierce and brave,
   Answered, "Yes, my captain."
   "Muster your crew,
   Brave veterans and sailors,
   Muster them all on deck."

4. The bosun blows his pipe,
   "On deck! – Loose the t'gallants!
   Shake out the reefs, we've a stern wind;
   Let us approach each other,
   And see who'll be the stronger."

5. "Haul the boat! Heave to!"
   We attacked her fore 'n' aft,
   Struck with boarding axes,
   With pikes and musketoons,
   We made her see reason.

6. And what will people say of her,
   In England and Breslau,
   Letting herself be taken,
   By a privateer of six cannons,
   She having thirty-six good ones?

LE GRAND COUREUR

FRENCH: CAPSTAN SONG

This is another French privateer or pirate song dealing with the days of bickering between the French and English. It is sung in a humorous vein, though much of the humor is lost in translation. A tradesman's job unknown in English ships, except ashore in shipyards, is that of the caulker – the *calfat* – mentioned in the second verse. The touching last verse, suggesting a "tip" in the way of booze, is of a type found at the end of folksongs of many countries.

Le cor- sair Le Grand Cou- reur, est un'
na- vir' de mal- heur, Quand il se met en croi-
sière, pour al- -ler chas-ser l'Ang-lais, le vent, la mer,
et la guer-re tour-nent con-tre le Fran-çais!
Al-lons les gars, gai, gai, al-lons les gars, gai-ment!

2. Il est part' de Lorient, avec bell' mer et bon vent,
   Il cinglait bâbord amure, naviguant comme un poisson,
   Un grain tombe sur sa mâture, v'là le corsaire en ponton !

3. Il nous fallut remâter, et bougrement bourlinguer,
   Tandis que l'ouvrage avance, on signale par tribord,
   Un navire d'apparence, à mantelets de sabords.

4. C'tait un Anglais vraiment, à double rangée de dents,
   Un marchand de mort subite, mais le Français n'a pas peur,
   Au lieu de brasser en fuite, nous le rangeons à l'honneur !

5. Ses boulets pleuvent sur nous, nous lui rendons coup pour coup,
   Pendant que la barbe en fume à nos braves matelots,
   Dans un gros bouchon de brume, il nous échappe aussitôt !

6. Nos prises au bout de six mois ont pu se monter à trois,
   Un navir' plein de patates, plus qu'à moitié chaviré,
   Un deuxième de savates, et le dernier de fumier !

7. Pour nous refair' des combats, nous avions à nos repas,
   Des gourganes et du lard rance, du vinaigre au lieu de vin,
   Du biscuit pourri d'avance, et du camphre le matin.

8. Pour finir ce triste sort, nous venons périr au port,
   Dans cette affreuse misère, quand chacun s'a vu perdu,
   Chacun selon sa manière, s'a sauvé comme il a pu !

9. Le cap'taine et son second, s'ont sauvés sur un canon,
   Le maître sur le grand ancre, le commis dans son bidon,
   Ah ! Le sacré vilain cancre, le voleur de rations !

10. Il eût fallu voir le coq, et sa cuiller et son croc,
    Il s'est mis dans sa chaudière, comme un vilain pot-au-feu,
    Il est parti vent arrière, atterrit au feu de Dieu !

11. De notre horrible malheur, seul la calfat est l'auteur,
    En tombant de la grand'hune, dessus le gaillard d'avant,
    A r'bondi dans la cambuse, a crevé le bâtiment !

12. Si l'histoire du Grand Coureur a pu vous toucher le coeur,
    Ayez donc belles manières, et payez-vous largement,
    Du vin, du rack, de la bière, et nous serons tous contents !

THE GREAT RACER

1. The corsair, the *Great Racer*, is an ill-omened ship,
   When she sets sail to hunt the English,
   The wind, the seas, and the fight, all go against the French.
   Ch.: Let's go, lads, cheerily, cheerily, let's go lads, so gaily!

2. She comes from Lorient with a good wind and sea,
   She was hauling out on the port tack, sailing like a fish,
   When a squall struck her tophamper an' the corsair was hulked.

3. We had to re-mast her, an' work like the devil,
   While the job was progressin', there signaled from starboard,
   A fine ship with port-covers on her guns.

4. An Englishman, in truth, with a double row of teeth,
   Carrier of sudden death, but the Frenchman has no fear,
   Instead of tryin' to escape, we challenge them to fight.

5. Their fire it rained upon us, we returned it shot for shot,
   While her beard was singeing, in a great cloud of smoke,
   She sailed away an' soon escaped us.

6. At the end of six months our prizes amounted to
                              [nothing more than three,
   One ship, half sunk an' full of spuds,
   The second with slippers for cargo, the third loaded with manure.

7. To recuperate from our fights, we had for our meals,
   Dried beans and rancid bacon, vinegar instead of wine,
   Biscuits long since rotten, an' morning camphor instead of coffee.

8. At the end of this fateful voyage, was our sinking as we made the port,
   In this frightful distress, when each seaman saw himself lost,
   We had to save ourselves, each one the best way he could.

9. The captain and his mate saved themselves on a gun,
   The master using the great anchor, the steward in his grog-tub,
   Ah, the wicked, bloody beggar, the robber of our rations!

10. You should have seen the cook, with his spoon an' meat-hook,
    He got into his pot, like a horrid stew,
    He went like the wind, made land like a thunderbolt.

11. For our horrible misfortune, the one responsible was the caulker,
    Who, falling from the main-top, over the forecastle,
    Bounced through the galley and smashed up the ship.

12. If this story of the *Great Racer* has touched your hearts,
    Have then the good manners to give generously,
    Wine, rum, or beer, an' we shall all be happy.

DANGER AND VIOLENCE; SHIPS (FACTUAL AND OTHERWISE)

We don't know when wind was first harnessed by man, but we do know that it gave him the opportunity to move across the water with the same facility as he moved on land. When early navigators discovered the trade winds the impetus to explore the world was furthered. Then they came across great gales the likes of which they'd never known in the Middle Sea — tornadoes and typhoons more powerful than the mistral or sirocco, hurricanes and pamperos far more destructive than a Tramontana or a Levanter. Through the ages there have been so many historical storms and shipwrecks, starting with St. Paul's shipwreck on the island of Melita (Malta), that it would take many volumes to chronicle them all. Some major wrecks are those of the East Indiaman *Grosvenor,* which broke up on the southwest coast of Africa in 1782; the *Centaur,* lost in the Atlantic in the same year; the terrible wreck of the Frenchman *Medusa* on the coast of Guinea in 1816; and the loss of the gold-ship *Royal Charter* on the rocks of Anglesey (1859). In more recent times we have the total loss of the ship *Strathmore* on the Crozets; the four-masted bark *Swanhilda* on Staten Island, near the Horn; the magnificent five-masted Danish *Kobenhavn* (1928) in the South Atlantic; the Finnish *Herzogin Cecilie* (1936) off Salcombe; and the last British square-rigger *Garthpool,* in the Cape Verde Islands in 1929 — which I was aboard at the time.

In a gale the upper sails are taken in off the mizzenmast first, the foremast next, and the mainmast last, along with the hauling down of the upper stays'ls, jibs, and spanker. After all the royals and t'gallants'ls are stowed, a ship would now be under six tops'ls, a reefed fores'l, say, and a fore-topmast stays'l. Under this rig she could weather out most storms, but if things got worse and the tops'ls blew away she would then be under "bare poles." In extremis, the only method of keeping a ship's head to the wind would be to "put a cloth in the rigging"; i.e., shoot part of a bolt of canvas up the weather mizzen rigging. This could happen in a typhoon, for instance.

Cannibalism in the days of sail was an only too frequent tragedy according to old-time logs. Survivors in open boats, mainly whalemen, had to resort to it in order to survive. Owen Chase, the mate of the whaleship *Essex,* sunk by the charge of a sperm whale, is said never to have forgotten the shortage of food and subsequent cannibalism in his boat; thereafter he hoarded up daily from Nantucket Main Street Market. After Captain Pollard of the *Essex* retired from the sea a reporter visited him. As he closed his interview the reporter

said he was a distant relative of a member of the crew of the *Essex*. "Did you know him?" he queried. "Know him?" answered Pollard. "Hell, son, I ate him!" Of course, in the early 1800s the crews of many whalers, sandalwood traders, and "blackbirders" were often "cut-out" by the natives of Melanesia, the Fiji Islands, and New Zealand, finishing up in these cannibals' stock-pots.

A ship has been described as the only man-made movable object in which human beings, for months and even years, actually live and have their being. At sea a sailing ship had no contact with the outside world. No two ships were ever alike; even sister ships, identically built and coming off the same stocks, performed differently when in the water. Exact duplicates of the famous *Marco Polo* ("Hell or Melbourne in sixty days!") were a flop and never made any records. A lot depended on the ship's captain; a good "handler" – Bully Forbes for instance – produced record-breaking passages. The *Cutty Sark* is world-famed for her speed, but under one master, Bruce, a drunkard and phony psalm-singer, she could hardly have claimed to be a clipper.

A ship is considered to be feminine – "she" – and just like any woman, she can be beautiful, a jade, unpredictable and cunning, and needs firm handling. That she was a living thing and had a soul, no sailor doubted. In Viking times this soul was not in her until put there at the ceremony of the "Roller Reddening" *(hlun rod)*, the blood from the human rollers and the hanging of a

head on her prow filling her instantly with spirit.

At one time a sailor would not join a ship if her figurehead were missing – she was "soulless," he'd say. The magnificent figureheads of the seventeenth century, which reached perfection in Swedish and French fighting ships, were not as golden as they appeared to be – only the royal coats of arms were of gold leaf, the rest were painted with a yellow concoction of white lead and Stockholm tar. This coloring was also used on the carvings of the quarter galleries. Eventually English men-o'-war settled for a lion (a rather *Chinoise* one) as a figurehead, which the French copied – possibly to baffle their enemies. The English,

in turn, copied the lines of French frigates, those of Sané being particularly well designed.

With their fine frigates the French should have done better in their sea fights with the English, but they didn't have the gunners. English fighting ships always tried to gain a weather gauge, firing downward into the "dead-work" or hull of an enemy ship, whereas the French tried to disable the masts and sails of an English ship by firing upward. In days of yore mutinies were fairly numerous in both naval and merchant ships, the most famous in the British Navy being those of H.M.S. *Bounty* and *Spithead* and the *Nore* (1797). However, among merchant-ship mutinies the most savage was that aboard the American ship *Frank N. Thayer,* en route from Manila to New York with a cargo of jute in 1886. In this mutiny two Manila men overpowered a crew of twenty, killed five men, wounded five, and set fire to the 1600-ton vessel. The mutineers, both wounded, jumped overboard and eventually disappeared in the sea, while the survivors left the stricken ship in boats and after a nine-day passage reached Jamestown, St. Helena, to tell their terrifying tale to the American consul.

138

BARNEY BUNTLINE

ENGLISH: FOREBITTER

This song is obviously a nautical skit on the dangerous life shore people live during storms and so on, in contrast to the "safe" life seamen enjoy in similar circumstances. Many sailorsongs adopt this attitude toward shore folk, even though deep in their hearts every seaman is aware – even in our day of container ships and giant tankers – that the sea is cruel and must be treated accordingly.

Caution and awareness are watchwords of today's seamen; how much more so would such words have applied in the days of "stick an' string!"

One night came on a hurricane, the sea wuz mountains rollin', When Barney Buntline chewed his quid an' said to Billy Bowline, "A strong nor'wester's blowin', Bill; hark, don't ye hear it roar now? Lord help 'em, 'ow I pities 'em unhappy folks on shore now." With a tow, row, row, Right to me ad-dy, Wi' a tow, row, row!

2. "An' as for them what lives in towns, what dangers they be all in,
An' now lay quakin' in their beds for fear the roof should fall in;
While you an' I, Bill, on the deck are comfortably lyin'.
My eyes! What tiles an' chimney pots about their heads are flyin'!"

3. "An' as for them what's out all day on business from their houses,
Returnin' home so late at night to cheer their babes an' spouses,
Poor creatures how they envy us an' wishes, I've a notion,
For our good luck in such a storm to be upon the ocean."

4. "Both you and I have oftimes heard how men are killed an' undone,
By overturn of carriages, by thieves, and fires of London.
We know what risks all landsmen run, from noblemen to tailors.
Then, Bill, let us thank Providence that you and I be sailors."

FRISCH AUF MIT ALLE MANN AN DECK

GERMAN: FOREBITTER AND
CAPSTAN SHANTY

This German forebitter and shanty is not in the usual Plattdeutsch and is a little more sentimental than the typical German seasongs. It was very popular however with the Jan Maats out of Hamburg. I, too, have joined in the singing of it as late as 1928 aboard a four-masted bark out of Bremen.

Frisch auf mit al-le Mann an Deck, Hol-la
hi, hol-la he, hol-la ho! Her- aus aus des ho-
gis Ver--steck, Ho-la hi, ho-la he, hol-la ho! Es
braust ein wü-ten- der Or-kan, O Män-ner rasch greift
an, greift an, Ho-la hi, hol-la he, hol-la ho!

In the first verse there is a reference to the *Orkan* – the hurricane. In 1957 one of the last of Germany's sail-training ships, the *Pamir*, was hit by a hurricane in the Atlantic on a passage home from Buenos Aires. She carried a cargo of grain in bulk – a dangerous cargo under canvas – was sailing under six tops'ls, fores'l (possibly reefed), inner jib, and topmast stays'ls, and was running before the wind when the hurricane caught her and threw her on her beam ends. Only six men survived from her complement of eighty-six hands. At the Court of Inquiry in Lubeck, all sorts of theories were put forward to explain how she was lost; but I reckon most sailing-ship men would give the grain in bulk as the deciding factor in her not righting herself.

140

LIVELY THERE, ALL HANDS ON DECK

2. Hurra schnell refft die Segel ein,
   Macht alles fest, was gross und klein,
   Fasst Mut und trotzet der Gefahr,
   Worin schon mancher Seemann war.

3. Hört wie der Grossmast knarrt und kracht,
   Er trotzet kühn des Sturmes Macht,
   Seht wie der Blitz am Horizont,
   Sich streitet mit dem Silbermond.

4. Die Wellen heben uns empor,
   Als wenn es ging zum Himmelstor,
   Und wieder geht es rasch bergab,
   Als zög man uns ins tiefe Grab.

5. Ha, eine Sturzsee über Deck,
   Wer sich nicht hält, den spült sie weg,
   Das Ruder fest in Männershand,
   Gut abgehalten von dem Strand,

6. Der Kapitän sieht mit Bedacht,
   Des wütenden Orkanes Macht,
   Teilt wichtige Befehle aus,
   Denkt an sein Weib und Kind zu Haus.

7. Ihr in der Kissen weichem Schoss,
   Seht her, das ist des Seemanns Los!
   Wenn ihr dort beim Champagner sitzt,
   Wie in Gefahr der Seemann schwitzt.

8. Schaut her, Ihr Schwelger in der Nacht,
   Umringt von Liebe und von Pracht,
   Seht, zwischen Himmel, Meer, und Tod,
   Sucht sich der Seemann nur sein Brot.

9. Drum achtet jeden Seemann hoch,
   Bedenkt, er trägt ein schweres Joch,
   Die Ehre und der grösste Ruhm,
   Sie sind des Seemanns Eigentum.

1. Oh, lively there, all hands on deck!
   Ch.: Hol-la hi, hol-la he, hol-la ho!
   No trying for to save your necks,
   Ch.: Hol-la hi, hol-la he, hol-la ho!
   There's blowin' now one hell of a gale,
   All hands hang lively, snug down sail!
   Ch.: Hol-la hi, hol-la he, hol-la ho!

2. Up boys an' reef them tops'ls tall,
   Make all things fast both big and small,
   Pick up your courage, show you're stout,
   What damn fine fellows, let 'em shout.

3. Oh, hear the mainmast creak and crack,
   The mighty wind is roaring back,
   The lightning on the horizon,
   Is battlin' with the silver moon.

4. The seas are risin' – great in size,
   They're racin' up toward the skies.
   A big one 'scends, the rollin' wave,
   As if to drag us to a sailor's grave.

5. A great sea lands upon the deck,
   If ye don't look out 'twill wash your neck,
   The man at the wheel grips the spikes in his hand,
   To keep her 'way off from the land.

6. The Old Man weighs his chances again,
   And the strength of the hellish hurricane,
   He then shouts out his orders clear,
   And thinks of his wife and children dear.

7. And you there on your pillows soft,
   Just think how hard is a seaman's lot,
   While you sit drinkin' of your wine,
   For sailors it is "Rise an' shine!"

8. Look! You there on a wild night's spree,
   With Love and Beauty on your knee,
   Between the sea and sky half dead,
   So works the seaman for his bread.

9. Then sing his praises, all you folk,
   With a stout heart he wears his yoke,
   Honor, esteem, and glory, too,
   These are our splendid sea-folk's due.

UN PETIT' NAVIRE

FRENCH: FOREBITTER

As well as shipwrecks, storms, and sea-fights, one of the other vicissitudes of a sailor's life in the days of sail was the prospect of cannibalism. After a ship had foundered, the crew got away in their small boats to suffer hell from thirst and starvation. Many sailorsongs tell of such events, and how in some cases, when all hope of salvation has vanished, the starved crew decides to eat the weakest or sickest member of the boat's crew. Sometimes in these songs the proposed victim is not eaten but is saved at the last moment by the appearance of a ship (or land), usually after the victim has been given the chance to pray. This song was a popular one among Breton sailors, and a rendition of it was known to French-Canadian seamen. In some versions the prayer of the boy is answered, in others it is not.

Il é-tait un pe-tit' na-vi-re, Il é-tait
un pe-tit' na-vi-re, Qui n'a-vait ja-ja-ja-mais
na-vi-gué, Qui n'a-vait ja-ja-ja-mais na-vi-gué.

2. Au bout de cinq à six semaines,
   Les vivres vinrent à manquer.

3. On fit tirer la courte paille,
   Pour savoir qui serait mangé.

4. Le sort tomba sur le plus jeune,
   En sauce blanche il fut ange.

5. Il monta sur le mat de hune,
   Et vit la mer de tous côtés.

6. "O Sainte Vierge, O ma patronne,
   Preservez-mois de ce danger."

7. Des p'tits poissons dans le navire,
   Sautèrent par milliers.

8. On les prit, on les mit à frire
   Le jeune mousse fut sauvé.

9. Si cette histoire vous amuse,
   Nous allons la recommencer.

A LITTLE SHIP

1. There once was a little ship,
   Which never got very far.

2. At the end of five or six weeks
   The grub became short.

3. The sailors drew straw lots
   To see who should be eaten.

4. The lot fell to the youngest,
   In white sauce they'd eat him.

5. The lad climbed up the topmast,
   Seeing only the sea.

6. "O, Holy Virgin, my guardian saint,
   Protect me from harm."

7. A hundred thousand fishes flew aboard
   And lay on the deck.

8. The sailors ate the fishes
   And the boy was saved.

9. If you've enjoyed this song,
   We'll sing it once again.

THE SHIP IN DISTRESS

ENGLISH: FOREBITTER

This story of a shipwrecked sailor being providentially saved from the fate of being eaten is one that dates back to the sixteenth century. In many European countries a similar tale is told in song. Another English song with this theme is "Three Sailors of Bristol City," a slightly altered form of Thackeray's "Little Billie." The latter, in turn, was based on another French song with a cannibalistic theme, "La Courbe Paille." Portuguese sailors also have a song telling a similar story, called "A Nau Catarineta."

You seamen bold that plow the ocean, See
dangers landsmen never know, It's not for
honor nor promotion. No tongue can tell what
they undergo. In bitter storms an' the
great wide water, Our ship went driftin'
o'er the sea, Her head-gear gone and her rudder
broken, Which brought us to extremity.

True stories of cannibalism in boats are only too numerous. In 1821 the American whaleship *Essex*, in the South Pacific, northeast of the Marquesas, was attacked by a huge sperm whale and eventually caused the ship to founder. The officers and crew got away in three whaleboats. Owen Chase, the chief mate, told the story when he was rescued. In the captain's boat, of the seven men aboard, one black seaman was eaten; in Chase's boat, one white man was eaten; and in the third boat, three black seamen were devoured. The captain's boat and Chase's boat were eventually saved but the third boat was never heard of again.

2. For fourteen days, thirsty an' hungry,
Nothing but water an' brazen sky,
Poor fellows stood they in a totter,
A-drawin' straws seeing who would die.
The lot it fell to Andrew Jackson,
Whose family was so very great,
"I'm free to die, but, oh, my shipmates,
Let me climb aloft till the dawn do break."

3. A full-rigged ship, like the sun a-glittering,
Came bearing down to their relief,
As soon as this glad news was shouted,
It banished hunger and their grief.
The ship hove to, no longer drifting,
Soon Isle Saint Vincent, Cape Verde, she gained.
Ye seamen all, now hear my story,
Pray ye'll never suffer the likes again.

RUDE BOREAS

ENGLISH: FOREBITTER

This curious song, from internal evidence, probably dates from the early 1700s. Its stanzas would appear to have been composed, alternately, by a seaman and a landsman. The seaman-like verses are impeccable in their seamanship; the others are built in the manner of the romantic shore ballads of the period. It has been suggested that it was composed by G. A. Stevens in 1754, but actually it was only popularized by him. At any rate, in the period when the broadside printers churned out hundreds of such ballads — many rubbish and of inaccurate seamanship — this song had a good enough nautical ring to it for sailors to accept it in their repertoires. In my grandfather's day it was popular among naval tars, and he taught it to my father who sang it to me often. In the middle passages a certain amount of syncopation was employed. Such a jazz effect, with "twiddles and quavers," was common in this type of forebitter.

Above: A storm at sea is rough on the whole crew!
Five views of the Belisarius *in rough seas, under* (left to right): *1. reefed foresail; 2. goosewings of foresail; 3. reefed mizen staysail; 4. reefed foresail close mizen staysail; 5. close reefed main topsail and foresail.*

1

2

2. Hark the bosun's hoarsely bawlin', by tops'l sheets an' halyards stand,
Down yer stays'ls, hard, boys, hard, down t'gallants quick be hauling,
See it freshens, set taut the braces, tops'l sheets now let go;
Luff, boys, luff; don't make wry faces, up yer tops'ls nimbly clew.

3. Now all ye on down beds a-sportin', fondly locked in Beauty's arms,
Fresh enjoyments, wanton courtin', safe from all but love alarms,
Round us roars the angry tempest, see what fears our minds enthrall,
Harder yet, it blows still harder, hark again the bosun's call.

4. The tops'l yard points to the wind, boys, see all clear to reef each course;
Let the foresheet go, don't mind boys, tho' the weather should be worse;
Fore 'n' aft the sprits'l yard get, reef the mizzen, see all clear,
Hands up each preventer-brace get, man the fore-yard, cheer, boys, cheer!

5. All the while fierce thunder roaring, peel on peel contending flash,
On our heads fierce rain falls pourin', in our eyes blue lightning's flash,
All around us one wide water, all above us one black sky,
Different deaths at once surround us, Hark! What means that dreadful cry?

6. "The foremast's gone!" cried every tongue out, o'er the lee twelve foot above deck.
A leak there is beneath the chesstree sprung, pipe all hands to clear the wreck;
Come cut the lanyards all to pieces, come, me hearts, be stout an' bold,
Plumb the well, the leak increases, four foot water in the hold.

7. On the lee beam there is land, boys, let the guns overboard be thrown,
To the pump, come every hand, boys; see our mizzenmast is gone!
The leak we've found; it can't pour faster, we've lightened her a foot or more.
Up an' rig a jury foremast. She's right, she's right, boys, we're off shore.

8. Now once more on shore we're thinkin', since kind heaven has saved our lives,
Come the cup, now let's be drinkin', to our sweethearts an' our wives,
Fill it up, about ship wheel it, close to our lips a-brimmin' fine,
Where's the tempest? Now, who feels it? None! the danger's drowned in wine!

"All Hands to the Pump" (above), by
H.S. Tuke, engraved by O. Lacour.

4   5

SKEPPET BERNADOTTE

SCANDINAVIAN: CAPSTAN

This is another shanty about a starvation-run, workhouse packet of a hulk. It is of Norwegian origin and Sternvall writes that his informant said he often sang it aboard the ship *Larvik* in 1904–05. The last couplet of each stanza was repeated as a refrain.

One may wonder why there are so many sailor-composed songs and shanties complaining about the ship in question, the captain, officers, grub, and work, but one must bear in mind that in the days of sail the majority of shipowners were tight-fisted, the majority of shipmasters disciplinarians — they *had* to be. Also it was considered a sailor's privilege to growl. "Growl ye may, but go ye must" was an old-time nautical adage, and it is said that a master who never heard his crew growling would be suspicious of his hands, thinking them to be plotting mutiny.

Med skep-pet Ber-na-dot-te till Car-diff vi gick, Å där-ri-från vi skul-le till Ba-hi-a gå, Å vår kä-ra-ste kap-tein vi i Car-diff ha-de mist, Å Små-brö-Hans vi ha-de fått, fått, fått. Å vär fått---.

2. *Vi styrte ut roveret å en följig vind vi fick,*
   De dröjde inte länge förr än bramsjla gick,
   De braka å de knaka a de blev ett fasligt spark,
   Uti detta gam la plunderverk, verk, verk.

3. *Vindpumpen akter ut den å som den kan,*
   Ja, den vill inte gå, ja, den giver inte vann,
   Ja, för att den skall gå må det blåsa en orkan,
   A da länsar hon på atten tommer vann, vann, vann.

4. *Å åtta dager efter sen vi va gångna ut,*
   Kom Småbrö- Hans å malte att brödet tagit slut,
   Tolv påsar där blev sydda, ja en till varje man,
   För att brödet skulle hålla ut till lann, lann, lann.

THE SHIP *BERNADOTTE*

1. We sailed away to Cardiff town,
   From there to Bahia we were bound,
   In Cardiff we lost our fine Old Man,
   And Hard-tack Hans we got, got, got.
   (Repeat last two lines in each verse as chorus)

2. With a following wind we steered away,
   The t'gallants blew out the following day,
   They boomed and they shook, made a dreadful kicking,
   In that very old piece of loot, loot, loot.

3. Being what it is – the windmill pump,
   Would neither go, nor suck a drop,
   Yes, for it to work it must blow a hurricane,
   And so we pumped out eighteen inches – water, water, water.

4. One week of this soon got us down,
   "The bread's nearly gone," said Hard-tack Hans,
   Twelve packets were made – one for each man –
   To whack out the bread till we came to land, land, land.

146

DET HÄNDE SIG I GÖTEBÖRG

SWEDISH: CAPSTAN SONG

This capstan song was popular aboard Swedish ships around 1870. The ship in this song is another *Bernadotte* – a name apparently well liked by Scandinavian shipowners.

Although she was a "splendid" brig, and aft they lived very well indeed, up for'ard in the fo'c'sle, what with the "rotten pork" and so on, and the master "a right martinet" to boot, it must have been a very different kettle of fish.

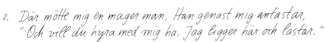

2. Där mötte mig en mager man, Han genast mig antastar,
   "Och vill du hyra med mig ha, Jag ligger här och lastar."

3. Och briggens namn var Bernadotte, Och skepparns namn *var Pelle,*
   De sa det var en duktig karl, Men fan var det i ställe.

4. Bernadotte är en duktig brigg, Hon bukar massingsnaglar,
   Och 'runda' ikring topparna, Gör vi var söndagsmorgon.

5. Och akterut du lever gott, Med allehanda rätter,
   I skansen får vi ruttet fläsk, Och fjorton ganger ärter.

6. Och Pelle, han låg nu och sov, Så hela skutan knarra,
   Så törna vi på Marstrands skär, Så masterna de darra.

7. Det hände sig i Spanska sjön, Vi skulle reva focken,
   Och 'Gubben' han blev något vred, Han börja prygla kocken.

8. Han sedan uppa halvdäck gick, Där gick han och fundera,
   Han sade: "Om jag vågar mej, Jag skulle prygla flera."

IT HAPPENED IN GOTHENBURG

1. It happened in Gothenburg, at the stroke of four o'clock,
   I took myself to Kusten' wharf, just to find myself a ship.
   Ch.: Hey ho, fallerallera! Hey ho, fallerallera!
         Just to find myself a ship!

2. There I met a very thin man, he hailed me right at once,
   "And will you sign on with me now, I'm lying here and loading?"

3. And the brig's name was *Bernadotte*, and the skipper's name was
   [Peter,
   They said he was a decent bloke, instead he was a devil.

4. *Bernadotte* is a splendid brig, with brass belayin' pins,
   And we inspect the rigging, every blessed Sunday morning.

5. If you live aft then you live well, with every kind of dishes,
   The fo'c'sle just has rotten pork, and peas fourteen times running.

6. And Peter now he lay and snored, so that the whole ship quivered,
   Then we struck on Marstrand's rocks, so hard that the masts
   [shiver'd,

7. It happened then in the Spanish Seas, that we should reef the fores'l,
   But the Old Man he blew his top and began to paste the cook.

8. Then after that upon the poop, he paced and paced and thought,
   He said: "If I only dared, I should paste the lot of you."

BLOW, BOYS, BLOW

AMERICAN/ENGLISH:
HALYARD SHANTY

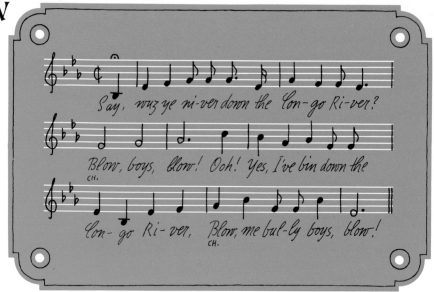

Say, wuz ye ni-ver down the Con-go Ri-ver?

Blow, boys, blow! Ooh! Yes, I've bin down the
CH.

Con-go Ri-ver, Blow, me bul-ly boys, blow!
CH.

This is one of the trio of famous Western Ocean packet shanties; the other two are "Blow the Man Down" and "Blackball Line." Some people seem to think that this song originated in the Guinea slaving trade, but the possibility that it was born in the days of the packet trade (1818) seems more likely. The reference to the slaving trade probably refers to certain disreputable skippers and shipowners who allowed their vessels to do a spot of slaving, and even piracy, after the 1820s when the slavers and pirates of the West Indies and the Guinea Coast were partly cleaned up by the joint efforts of America and several European powers. The verse about "black sheep that have run the Embargo" points to latter-day slaving, since the Embargo was not enforced until about 1820. After the first two verses references to the slaving trade have been lost; the more modern version is another skit about the "Harry Tate" ship and her comic-opera crew.

The names of the masters and mates found in other versions are as follows: Pompey Squash, the big buck nigger; Bully Hayes, the Down East bucko; Big Black Jack, the Boston Slugger; Cockeyed Bill, the West End Barber; Santander James, the Rocket from Hell; Nigger Dick from New Brunswick; A Bow-legged Bastard from the Bowery.
Other forms of food are: sharks' fins and monkey's liver; mosquito's heart and sandfly's liver; dandy funk and centipede's whiskers; nanny goat's horns and a donkey's rudder.
And for cargo: five hundred bottles of German lager; four hundred chimps from Santiago.

2. Congo she's a mighty river,
   Where the fever makes the white man shiver.

3. A Yankee ship came down the river,
   Her masts and yards they shine like silver.

4. How d'yer know she's a Yankee clipper?
   By the blood an' guts that flow from her scuppers.

5. How d'yer know she's a Yankee packet?
   She fired her guns an' we heard the racket.

6. She's Yankee ship an' she's bound for China,
   An' a bunch of bastards they have joined her.

7. Who d'yer think's the skipper of her?
   Bully Waterman's the skipper of her.

8. Who d'yer think's the chief mate of her?
   Some ugly case what 'ates poor sailors.

9. Saccarappa Jim is the second mate of her,
   He'll ride you down like ye ride a spanker.

10. What d'yer think they had for dinner?
    Belayin'-pin soup an' a roll in the scuppers.

11. What d'yer think they had for cargo?
    Black sheep that have run the Embargo.

12. Blow today an' blow tomorrow,
    Blow for this ol' ship in sorrow.

DE HAMBORGER VIERMASTER

PLATTDEUTSCH: CAPSTAN

This is the Plattdeutsch version of the American capstan song "Sacramento." It was very popular in ships of the Laiesz line of Hamburg engaged in the Chilian nitrate trade, and was even heard aboard the German four-masted bark *Pamir* as late as 1952.

It is also said to be one of the very few German sailorsongs taught in school and known to most German school children. The English refrains of "Hoodah, hoodah!" are sung here as "Howday, howday!" The Norwegians, who also like this shanty, sang *"Ota Hayti, ota Hayti!"* – referring to the Pacific island of Tahiti; the Swedes, in their own language version, had *"O, Bermudas, O, Bermudas!"* Like many sailorsongs it is critical of the state of the old-time sailing ships – bad grub, rotten gear, a surfeit of bugs and weevils, rotten salt junk, and maggoty salt horse.

2. Dat deck weer von Isen, vull Schiet an vull Smeer,
   Dat weer Schietgäng eer schönstes Plaseer.

3. Dat Logis weer vull Wanzen, de Kombüüs weer vull Dreck,
   De Beschüten de lopen von sulben all weg.

4. Dat soltfleesch weer gröön, un de Speck weer vull Maden,
   Kööm geev bloss an'n Winachtsabend.

5. Un wull'n wi mal seil'n, ik segg dat jo nur,
   Denn lööp he dree vörut un veer weerer retur.

6. As dat Schipp, so weer ok de Kaptein,
   De Lüüd för dat Schipp wörn ok bloss schanghait.

THE HAMBURG FOUR-MASTER

1. I once saw a Hamburg four-masted bark,
   Ch.: To me hoodah! To me hoodah!
   Her masts were as crooked as the Old Man's legs.

   Ch.: To me hoodah, hoodah, ho!
   Full ch.: Blow, boys, blow!
   For Californ-i-O!
   There's plenty of gold, so I've bin told,
   On the banks of the Sacramento!

2. Her decks were of iron, full of dirt and of muck,
   The ship-cleaners in harbor thought she was vile.

3. Her fo'c'sle full of bugs, her galley full of mud,
   The weevils they ran about freely.

4. The salt-meat was green, full of maggots the pork,
   The rum was dished out at Christmas alone.

5. When we were trying to sail this old tub,
   She'd sail ahead three and sail back four.

6. The captain was hopeless, the same as that ship,
   The crew for that packet were all shanghaied men.

149

THE DREADNAUGHT

AMERICAN/ENGLISH: FOREBITTER

Very few Anglo-Saxon sailorsongs are about named ships – this is one of the few. The *Dreadnaught* was a well-known North Atlantic packet ship that carried a red cross beneath the close-reef of the fore tops'l. She is renowned for a mutiny which once took place aboard her. A famous gang of tough Irish seamen, called the "Bloody Forty," noted for signing on in packet ships in order to give the afterguard much trouble, joined the *Dreadnaught* and started a mutiny.

Her master, Captain Samuels, with his famous Newfoundland dog Wallace, the second mate, and seventeen powerful German emigrants armed with iron

There is a flash pack-et, flash pack-et o'
fame, She hails from New York an' the Dread-naught's
name, She's bound to the west'ard where the wild wa-ters
flow, Bound a-way to the west-ard in the Dread-naught we'll
go! Der-ry down, down, down der-ry down!
CH.

2. The time of her sailin' is now drawin' nigh,
Stand by all ye lubbers, we wish you goodbye,
A pair of clean heels to you now we will show,
Bound away in the Dreadnaught to the west'ard we'll go!

3. An' now we are leavin' the sweet Salthouse docks,
The boys and the gals on the Pierhead do flock,
The boys an' the gals are all shoutin' hurro,
Bound away to the west'ard in the Dreadnaught we go!

4. Oh, the Dreadnaught's awaiting in the River Mersey,
Awaiting the tugboat to tow her to sea,
An' around the Rock Light where the salt tides do flow,
Bound away in the Dreadnaught to the west'ard we'll go!

5. An' now we are sailin' down the wild Irish Sea,
Our passengers are merry an' their hearts full o' glee,
Our sailors like tigers they walk to an' fro,
Bound away in the Dreadnaught to the west'ard we go!

6. Oh, now we are sailin' the Atlantic so wide,
An' the hands are now ordered to scrub the ship's side,
With her tops'ls set taut for the red cross to show,
Bound away in the Dreadnaught to the west'ard we'll go!

7. An' now we are sailin' the Banks o' Newf'n'land,
   Where the bottom's all fishes an' fine yellow sand,
   An' the fishes they sing as they swim to an' fro,
   She's the Liverpool packet, oh, Lord let her go!

8. Now the Dreadnaught's arrived in ol' New York town,
   We're bound for the Bowery an' let sorrow drown,
   With our gals an' our beer, boys, oh, let the song flow,
   We're the Liverpool packet, oh, Lord let her go!

9. Here's a health to the Dreadnaught and all her brave crew,
   To bold Cap'n Samuels an' his officers, too,
   Ye may talk of yer fliers, Swallowtail an' Blackball,
   But the Dreadnaught's the packet that outsails 'em all!

10. Now me story is ended an' me yarn it is told,
    Forgive me ol' shipmates if ye think that I'm bold,
    For this song was composed while the watch was below,
    Bound away to the west'ard in the Dreadnaught we'll go!

bars, managed to subdue the forty mutineers, the ringleaders of whom were Finnegan, Casey, and Sweeney. Food was refused the mutineers since they would not take in sail during a gale. After two days without food the men challenged the afterguard and a fight took place in the semi-darkness. Finally the mutineers gave in and threw their knives overboard, but Finnegan still defied the master. Samuels then struck the Irishman a powerful blow, knocking him down the fo'c'sle steps. He put Finnegan, ironed, in a "sweat-box," not allowing him out until Finnegan admitted defeat. The mutious hands left the ship in New York, cheering the old "tiger" Samuels as they went.

The *Dreadnaught* was wrecked in 1869 off the rugged cliffs of Cape Horn. She was one of the most handsome-looking of the packet ships.

BOUNTY WAS A PACKET SHIP

ENGLISH: PUMPING SHANTY

This brake-pump shanty tells the famous story of the mutiny on the *Bounty*. The captain's name, Bligh, is here sung as Blight – possibly a sailor pun on a nasty piece of work! In the light of recent historical research, there has been a tendency to exonerate Bligh a little in his handling of the crew and to point out that similar draconian measures were meted out to most seamen in those days. In other words he may have been the normal shipmaster of the times.

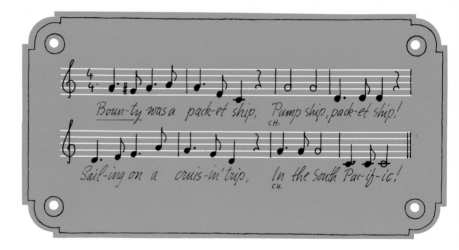

Boun-ty was a pack-et ship, Pump ship, pack-et ship! (CH.)
Sail-ing on a cruis-in'trip, In the South Pac-if-ic! (CH.)

Later, however, as governor of the New South Wales penal settlements, a similar situation arose between him and the convicts. This repetition makes him seem a proper martinet, worse even than his brother captains. In this light we feel that the words of the shanty may be true. The final verse (which states that the fate of the survivors was unknown) seems to indicate that the shanty originated late in the eighteenth century. Captain Jenkins, the source for the song, noted that the mutiny took place in 1789 and, until an American sealer (Captain Folger) discovered the mutineers on Pitcairn Island in 1809, the civilized world was ignorant as to their fate. Therefore the date of the shanty may be prior to 1809.

2. Billy Blight, that silly man,
Was the master in command.

3. He was growling day and night,
Whether he was wrong or right.

4. On the Bounty were the rules,
Not for soft an' silly fools.

5. An' the answer to complaints,
Handcuffs an' the iron chains.

6. Spittin' on the quarterdeck,
Punishment – a broken neck.

7. There were troubles every day,
Many sailors ran away.

8. An' at last that Billy Blight,
With his crew began to fight.

9. Brawling, kickin' everywhere,
Iron pins flew thro' the air.

10. Mates an' sailors in the night,
Overpowered Billy Blight.

11. They put Billy Blight afloat,
With his madness in a boat.

12. Bounty then went out of sight,
Left alone was Billy Blight.

13. Billy Blight he reached the coast,
But the Bounty she was lost.

14. Many gales have crossed the sea,
Since the Bounty went away.

15. Never was there heard a word,
From the crew that stayed on board.

152

LA PIQUE

ENGLISH: FOREBITTER

Immediately after the Napoleonic Wars, the English fleet had an easy time – for a while. Then came a period of mass unemployment. On admirals and cabin boys the austerity axe fell; and as some songs of the day tell, they had to find jobs blacking boots, selling matches, or begging on the streets of London. To keep the still employed men and officers actively engaged, all sorts of polishing and cleaning jobs were invented and smart sail maneuvers such as "About ship and reef tops'ls in one" were included as a daily ritual aboard every ship in the fleet of the Royal Navy.

Oh, 'tis of a flash fri-gate, La Pique was her name, All in the West In--dies she bore a great name, For cruel bad u--sage of ev'ry de-gree, Like slaves in the gal-ley we plowed the salt sea.

Such cleaning and maneuvers were introduced in the biblical belief that "Satan finds some mischief for idle hands to do," and the naval ships in which such extremes of work were the normal routine were referred to as "fancy frigates." The ship *La Pique* in our song was one such fancy frigate and it can be seen from the relevant verses that every tar was kept on his toes; those that cursed under their breath and rebelled against what they considered unnecessary discipline soon received "three dozen" of the cat-o'-nine-tails. The final verse advises all brother seamen to steer clear of such ships because "they'll haze ye…'till ye ain't worth a damn."

2. At four in the mornin' our work is begun,
To the cockpit the waisters for buckets must run,
Our fore an' main topmen so loudly do bawl,
For sand an' for holystones, both large an' small.

3. Our decks being washed down and mopped up quite dry,
'Tis lash up your hammocks our bosun do cry,
Our hammocks are lashed, black clews an' black snows,
An' all of one size, boy, thro' the hoops they must go.

4. An' now look aloft, oh, me boys, every one,
All hands to make sail, goin' large is the song,
From under two reefs in our tops'ls we lie,
Like a cloud all our canvas in a moment must fly.

5. An' now me brave boys comes the best of the fun,
It's hands about ship an' reef tops'ls in one,
Our hands go aloft when the helm it goes down,
Lower away tops'ls as the mainyard goes round.

6. Now your quids of tobacco I'd have ye to mind,
If ye spits on the deck, sure your death warrant's signed;
If ye spits over bow, over gangway or starn,
You're sure of three dozen just by way of no harm.

7. Come, all brother seamen, where'er ye may be,
From all fancy frigates I'd have ye steer free,
For they'll haze ye, an' work ye, 'till ye ain't worth a damn,
Then they'll ship ye half-dead to your dear native land.

LA DANAÉ

FRENCH: FOREBITTER
also used at the Capstan

This is another type of song beloved by the old-time sailor, wherein on being wrecked, or just stepping out of a boat, he meets on the beach a beautiful girl — for instance a mermaid seated on rocks with a comb and glass in hand, or a singing Lorelei.

Don't forget, even in the *Odyssey* it was only Odysseus, and in Jason's voyage, Jason — the captains of the ships concerned — who were tied to the mast or had their ears stuffed with cotton wool so as to avoid the lures of the Scyllas and Sirens of the clasical world. The mariners *wanted*, naturally, to meet such mythological beauties and the captains had a job to restrain them!

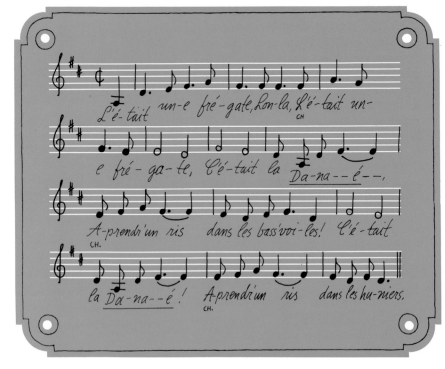

L'é-tait un-e fré-gate, Lon-la, L'é-tait un-e fré-ga-te, L'é-tait la Da-na--é--, A-prendr'un ris dans les bass'voi-les! L'é-tait la Da-na--é! A-prendr'un ris dans les hu-niers.

2. A son premier voyage, Lonla,
   La frégat' a sombré.

3. Et de tout l'équipage, Lonla,
   Un gabier s'a sauvé.

4. Il abord' sur la plage, Lonla,
   Il savait bien nager.

5. Mais là, sur le rivage, Lonla,
   Une bell' éplorée.

6. Belle comm'une frégate, Lonla,
   Française et pavoisée.

7. "Pourquoi pleurer la belle, Lonla,
   Pourquoi si tant pleurer ?"

8. "Je pleur'mon avantage, Lonla,
   Dans la mer qu'est tombé."

9. "Et qu'aurait donc la belle, Lonla,
   Celui qui vous l'rendrait ?"

10. "Lui en ferai offrande, Lonla,
    Avec mon amitié."

11. A la première plonge, Lonla,
    L'marin n'a rien trouvé.

12. A la centième plonge, Lonla,
    Le pauvre s'a noyé.

13. Car jamais avantage, Lonla,
    Perdu n'est retrouvé.

THE *DANAÉ*

1. There was a frigate, tra, la,
   (Repeat first line in each verse as chorus)
   She was the *Danaé,*
   Ch.: Take a reef in the courses!
   (Repeat second line in each verse)
   Ch.: Take a reef in the tops'ls!

2. Oh her first voyage, tra, la,
   The frigate sank.

3. And of all the crew, tra, la,
   A topman saved himself.

4. He gets ashore on the beach,
   He could swim.

5. But there on the beach,
   A tearful beauty.

6. As beautiful as a frigate,
   French, and decked with flags.

7. "Why are you weeping, fair one?
   Why are you weeping so much?"

8. "I am weeping for my favor,
   Which has fallen into the sea."

9. "And what would he have then, fair one?
   Who gave it back to you?"

10. "I shall offer it to him,
    With my friendship."

11. On the first dive,
    The sailor found nothing.

12. On the hundredth dive,
    The poor fellow got drowned.

13. For never is a lost favor,
    Found again.

LES FILLES DE LA ROCHELLE

FRENCH: FOREBITTER

This old forebitter was a favorite with the *matelot*, and in particular with my old shipmate Jean Loro, seaman from Nantes who once knew well the decks of the Borde sailing ships of Dunkerque. It has a fairylike quality about it, unlike other "Fille" songs that were so popular in French fo'c'sles; for example "La Fille de Sables" and "Les Filles de Camaret," both extremely bawdy.

2. *Le grand'vergue est en ivoire,*
   Les poulies en diamant.

   Le grand'voile est en dentelle,
   La misaine en satin blanc.

3. *Les cordages du navire,*
   Sont de fil d'or et d'argent,
   Et la coque est en bois rouge,
   Travaillé' fort proprement.

4. *L'équipage du navire,*
   C'est tout filles de quinze ans,
   Le cap'tain' qui les commande,
   Est le roi des bons enfants.

5. *Hier, faisant sa promenade,*
   Dessous le gaillard d'avant,
   Aperçut une brunette,
   Qui pleurait dans les haubans.

6. *"Qu'avez-vous gentill' brunette,*
   Qu'avez-vous à pleurer tant,
   Avez-vous perdu père, mère,
   Ou quelqu'un de vos parents?"

7. *"J'ai cueilli la rose blanche,*
   Qui s'enfut la voile au vent,
   Elle est partie vent arrière,
   Reviendra z'en louvoyant."

THE DAUGHTERS OF LA ROCHELLE

1. They are the daughters of La Rochelle,
   A fleet of ships,
   (Repeat second line in each verse)
   For to engage the foe,
   In the seas of the Levant.
   Ch.: Ah, the leaf flies away, flies away!
   Ah, the leaf flies away in the wind!

2. The main yard is of ivory,
   The blocks are made of diamonds,
   The mains'l is of lace,
   The fores'l of white satin.

3. The ropes of this ship
   Are of gold and silver thread,
   And the hull is of redwood,
   Worked handsomely.

4. The crew of this ship
   Are all fifteen-year-old girls,
   The master in charge
   Is king of these good children.

5. Yesterday while walking
   Upon the fo'c'slehead,
   He spotted a brunette
   Crying in the shrouds.

6. "What is the matter sweet brunette?
   Why are you crying so?
   Have you lost father, mother,
   Or one of your parents?"

7. "I picked the white rose,
   Which flew away in the wind.
   It was carried before the wind,
   Veering and tacking."

156

CLEAR THE TRACK

AMERICAN/ENGLISH: CAPSTAN SONG

This shanty was a great favorite in the Yankee packets of the early 1800s. Its tune is that of the Irish folksong "Shule Agra" but the refrains have wording showing Negro influence. It is a good example of the type of song that passed through what I call the "Shanty Mart" of New Orleans and other Gulf ports.

Ooh, the smart-est pack-et ye can find, Ah ho! Way ho! Are you 'mos' done? Is the ol' Wild Cat of the Swal-lowtail line, So! clear the track, let the bul-gine run! To-me high rig-a-jig in a jaunt-in' car, Ah ho! Way ho! Are you 'mos' done? Wid E-li-za Lee all on me knee, So! Clear the track, an' let the bul-gine run!

White sailors, in this case some Irish seamen, probably hummed their native ditties when ashore in the grog-ships of the Southern levees. The black and Creole stevedores – the cotton-stowing "Hoosiers" – heard them, liked them, and, with their own wording added, used them as chants to help when pressing the cotton bales into the holds of the droghers by means of the jack-screws. Visiting seamen would hear them, put nautical words to them, and turn them into use at capstan and halyards. Hence the origin of many sailor work songs. "Bulgine" is American-Negro slang for a "steam engine."

2. Oh, the ol' Wild Cat of the Swallowtail line,
   She's never a day behind her time.

3. Oh, we're outward bound for New York town,
   Them Bowery gals we'll waltz around.

4. Oh, the gals are walkin' on the pier,
   Let's all go ashore an' have some beer.

5. When we gits back to Liverpool town,
   I'll stand ye whiskies all around.

6. Oh, in Liverpool town them gals hang 'round,
   An' there me Liza she'll be found.

7. Oh, when I gits home across the sea,
   Eliza, will you marry me?

THE FLYING CLOUD

AMERICAN: FOREBITTER

Both American and British seamen sang this forebitter, although its origin was probably Irish or else Irish-American. In the song both slavery and piracy are mentioned, suggesting that the song dates back to sometime in the first half of the nineteenth century. Slavery was abolished in Jamaica and in British ships in 1807 and in America in 1863. Slavery and piracy often went hand in hand, and the naval gunboats concerned had quite a job running down these inhuman monsters.

Stories relating to the inhumanity of these slaving passages have filled many a book. One story, not well known, is as follows. In 1819 the French slaver *Le Rodeur* sailed from Bonny, West Africa, with a crew of twenty-two and 160 slaves. Nearing the equator a contagious eye disease broke out among the slaves, aggravated by the shortage of water (half a wine glass each day per man). The slave-ship's doctor brought some of the slaves up on deck at times, but the slaves, embracing each other, jumped overboard and drowned. As punishment for such disrespect to his wishes, the captain hung several of the slaves, and then later he had thirty-six of them, who had become incurably blind, thrown overboard as useless cargo. The French slaver then came across a Spanish slaver, the *Leon*. All of her crew and her black cargo had contracted the same disease and were completely blind; she was never heard of again. *Le Rodeur* reached Guadaloupe on 21 June, with only one man still able to see, though by the time the ship was berthed he had caught it too. Incidentally neither the *Flying Cloud* of the song nor her captain have been identified, both probably being fictitious.

My name is Ed-ward Hol-land-er as you may un-der-stand. I was born in the ci-ty of Wa-ter-ford, in E-rin's love-ly land. When I was young an' in me prime an' beau-ty on me shone, Me pa-rents do-ted on me, 'cos I was their on-ly son.

2. My father he rose up one morn an' wid him I did go;
   He bound me as a butcher boy to Kearny's of Wicklow.
   I wore the bloody apron there for three long years or more,
   Then I shipped aboard the Erin's Queen, the pride of ol' Tramore.

3. 'Twas when we reached Bermuda's Isle I met with Cap'n Moore,
   The master of the Flying Cloud, the pride of Baltimore;
   An' I undertook to sail wid him, on a slavin' voyage to go,
   To the burnin' shores of Africay, where the sugarcane do grow.

4. Oh, all went well until we came to Africay's burnin' shores,
   Five hundred of them slaves, me boys, from their native land we bore;
   Oh, each man loaded down wid chains as we made them march below,
   Just eighteen inches space, me boys, oh, each man had to show.

5. We sank an' plundered many a ship down on the Spanish Main,
   Left many a wife an' orphaned child in sorrow to remain,
   To them we gave no quarter but we gave them watery graves,
   For the sayin' of our capen was, "Dead men tell no tales."

6. An' now to Newgate we must go bound down wid iron chains,
   For the sinkin' an' the plunderin' of ships on the Spanish Main;
   The judge he found us guilty, an' we are condemned to die,
   Young man a warnin, by me take, an' shun all piracy!

158

EN GAMMAL BRIGG

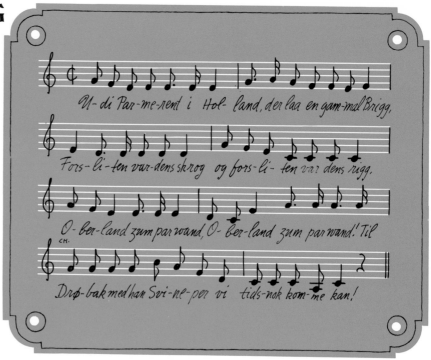

U-di Par-me-rent i Hol-land, der laa en gam-mal Brigg,
Fors-li-ten var-dens skrog og fors-li-ten var dens rigg,
O-ber-land zum par wand, O-ber-land zum par wand! Til
Drø-bak med han Svi-ne-per vi tids-nok kom-me kan!

NORWEGIAN: PUMPING SONG

This song in its original form was Norwegian, but there are Swedish (sung in the old sea-lingo), Scandinavian dialect, Danish, and German versions. The one we give here has in fact five different languages in its chorus. Verses 1 and 2 have choruses in a sort of German, 3 in Norwegian-Danish, 4 is in Norwegian, 5 in the Bergen dialect, and 6 is in Swedish.

2. Det fandtes ikke kompas eller nathaus ved dens ratt,
Vi styrte efter pullen i Per Svine's gamle hatt,
        Oberland zum par wand, oberland zum par wand,
        Till Drøbak med han Svineper vi tidsnok komme kan.

3. Kahytten den var umalt, men ruffen der var god,
Og Køierne var malte med vaeggelusblod,
        Overland som tibrands, overland som paa vand,
        Til Drøbak med den Griseper vi aldrig komme kan.

4. Vi maatte pumpe laens imellem hvert et glas,
Og naar vi gik fra haven, skar vi katten ind til bras,
        Gi mig ranson paa vand, gi mig ranson paa vand,
        Og fire mand i giggen satte Svineper iland.

5. Og naar vi først var kommet et stykke ut fra land,
Drak Svineper mer braendevin end alle mand drakvand,
        Hive langsomt fra land, hive langsomt fra land,
        De Bergenske møer snart møte nok vi kan.

6. Det var Søndagsmorna, vi blev purret ut til baut,
Men naar vi saa i luka, laa kjølsvinet og flaut,
        Kors i Herrans namn, hur det går langsomt fran land,
        Vi hurra för den resan, när vi kom til Köpenhamn.

THE OLD BRIG

1. Oh, in Parmerent in Holland, there lay an ancient brig,
   Worn out was her hull, boys, and rotten was her rig.
   Ch.: Overland as at sea, overland as at sea!
        To Drobak with the dirty old hog in welcome come we!

2. Oh, she had no steering compass, no wheelhouse standing aft,
   The sailors they did steer her by the crown of Per Svine's hat.
   Ch.: Overland as at sea, overland as at sea!
        To Drobak with the dirty old hog in welcome come we!

3. Her saloon was unpainted, the fo'c'sle weren't too good,
   The bunks they all were painted with stinkin' red bug's blood.
   Ch.: Overland as at sea, overland as at sea!
        To Drobak with the dirty old pig in welcome come we!

4. Watch and watch we pumped the ol' ship out, our backs were
                                    [just like lead,
   And once we left the harbor, boys, sweatin' braces we did dread.
   Ch.: Oh, the sea, let it roar! Oh, the sea, let it roar!
        Put four men in the longboat, boys, an' row the pig ashore!

5. And after we had sailed, me boys, and the land was still in sight,
   The pig it drank up all the rum an' very soon was tight.
   Ch.: Heave-O, slowly out to sea! Heave-O, slowly out to sea!
        The pretty girls of Bergen, oh, quite soon we all will see!

6. It was a Sunday morning, the hands for 'bout ship went,
   But when we glanced below, my lads, we found the keel was bent.
   Ch.: Oh, good Lord! Oh, good Lord! Oh, the land is still in sight!
        Hurrah, me boys, for a bloomin' fine trip and the
                                    Copenhagen Light!

THE EBENEZER

ENGLISH: PUMPING SONG

According to my source – Paddy Grif-fiths, an old Irish sailing-ship man – this rather humorous song was often sung at the pumps. It is fairly obvious that it is of Irish origin, or at least Liverpool-Irish, and maybe the air is an Irish fiddle tune. "Second greaser" is a Western Ocean packet-ship term for a second mate. A "Blackball cheeser" was the type of soft-crowned, peaked cap, with no stiffening in the crown, favored by windjammer men.

I shipp'd on board of the E-ben-e-zer, Ev'ry day 'twas scrub an' grease 'er, Send us a-loft to scrape 'er down. An' if we growl'd they'd blow us down. Oh, CH. git-a-long, boys, git-a long do, Han-dy, me boys, so han-dy! Git a-long, boys git-a-long do; Hun-dy, me boys, so han-dy!

2. The Old Man wuz a drunken geezer,
Couldn't sail the Ebenezer,
Learnt his trade on a Chinese junk,
He spent mos' time, sir, in his bunk.

3. The chief mate's name wuz Dickie Green, su
The dirtiest beggar ye've ev'r seen, sir,
Walkin' his poop wid a bucko roll,
May the sharks have his body an' the devil
have his soul.

4. A Boston buck wuz second greaser,
He used to ship in Limejuice ships, sir,
The Limey packets got too hot,
He jumped 'em an' he cursed the lot,

5. The bosun came from Tennessee, sir,
He always wore a Blackball cheeser,
He had a gal in every port,
At least that's what his Missus thought.

6. The Ebenezer wuz so old, sir,
She knew Columbus as a boy, sir,
'Twas pump her, bullies, night an' day,
To help her git to Liverpool Bay.

7. Wet hash it wuz our only grub, sir,
For breakf'st, dinner, an' for supper,
Our bread wuz as tough as any brass,
An' the meat wuz as salt as Lot's wife's ass.

ALBERTINA

SCANDINAVIAN:
CAPSTAN AND PUMPING SONG

This is the Swedish version of a song equally popular among all Scandinavian sailors. It is of Norwegian origin, and according to Captain Sternvall it was usual for the shantyman to imitate a Norwegian dialect when singing it. Prof. J. Glyn Davies contends that the tune is German. It is a song well known even among landsmen and survived, though not as a work song, until as late as the 1930s aboard Finnish sailing ships.

Det skall byg-gas ett skepp ut-i Nor-den,
Al-ber-ti-na skall va-ra skep-pets namn, Pum-pa
CH.
läns! Al-ber-ti-na lät så va-ra, Al-ber-
ti-na, in-gen fa-ra, Al-ber-ti---na skall
va-ra, skep-pets namn-Pum-pa läns! Al-ber-ti-na lät så
F.CH.
va-ra, Al-ber-ti-na in-gen fa-ra, Al-ber-
ti-na skall va-ra, skep-pets namn-Pum-pa läns!

2. Och det skepper är allaredan lastat,
   Det är lastat med bayerskt öl och vin,
   Det är lastat, låt så vara, det är lastat ingen fara,
   Det är lastat med bayerskt öl och vin – Pumpa läns!

3. Men på straden står Ingrid och gråter,
   Ja, hon gråter efter lilla vannen sin,
   Ja, hon gråter, låt så vara, ja, hon gråter, men vi fara,
   Ja, hon gråter efter lilla vännen sin – Pumpa läns!

4. Varje sjömans grav är redan gräven,
   Den är gräven i böljorna de blå,
   Den är gräven, låt så vara, den är graven, men vi fara,
   Den är gräven i böljorna de blå – Pumpa läns!

5. Och min gravskrift den är redan skriven,
   Den är skriven på finaste latin,
   Den är skriven, låt så vara, den är skriven, men vi fara,
   Den är skriven på finaste latin – Pumpa läns!

1. Oh, a ship will be built in the northland.
   O *Albertina* shall be that good ship's name;
   Ch.: Pump her dry!
   Albertina let it be then; *Albertina*, there's no danger;
   O, *Albertina* shall be that good ship's name – pump her dry!
   (*Repeat last two lines of each verse as full chorus*)

2. Oh, that ship she is already loaded,
   She is loaded up with good Bavarian beer,
   She is loaded, let it be then, she is loaded, there's no danger,
   She is loaded up with good Bavarian beer – pump her dry!

3. But on the shore stood Ingrid and she's weeping,
   Yes, weeping for her own and dearest friend,
   She is weeping, let it be then, she is weeping, now we're sailing,
   She is weeping for her own and dearest friend – pump her dry!

4. The grave of every sailor's dug already,
   His grave lies in the billows, oh, so blue,
   Graves are ready, let it be then, graves are ready, now we're sailing,
   The graves are lying in the billows, oh, so blue – pump her dry!

5. And my epitaph it is already written,
   It's written in the finest Latin script,
   It is written, let it be then, it is written, now we're sailing,
   It is written in the finest Latin script – pump her dry!

MAGELHAN

This is the Plattdeutsch version of the English capstan song "Rolling Home." The eight-line verses of the forebitter are twice as long as those in the shanty. As in "Der Hamborger Veermaster" and the English shanty "Leave Her Johnny, Leave Her," here again Jan Maat endeavors to show what a rotten old "basket" of a ship he's joined, what a workhouse she is, and what a son-of-a-gun the master is. Of course, sailors of all nations moaned about their present ship, their previous ship always being much better – usually the finest ship that ever sailed!

Dor weer een mol een ohlen Kassen, Een Klipper namens Mag-el'han. Dor weer bi Dag keen Tid tom Brassen, Det A-bends denn wör al-lens dahn, Det A-bends denn wör al-lens dahn, Bi dag dor kunn dat weihn un bla-sen, Dor wör noch lang keen Hand an-legt–; Doch slög det Klock man erst acht Gla-sen, Denn wör de gan-ze Plünn-krom streckt. Sing' val-le ra-le, ral-le-ral-le ra--la, ra--la, ra--la, Sing' val-le ral-le, ral-le-ral-le ra--la, Val-le--ri, val-le-ri, val-le-ra---!

2. *Dat weer so recht den Ooln sien Freten,*
   Dat gung em över Danz un Ball,
   Harr Janmaat graad een Pip ansteken,
   Dann grööl he: Pull in't Grootmarsfall.

   Dat kunn de Kerl verdüvelt seggen,
   He jöög uns rüm von Fall to Fall.
   Dat kunn man pullen, riten, trecken,
   Un kreeg gewöönlich kenen Toll.

3. *Un up den heil'gen, stillen Fridag,*
   Geevt middags gele Arfenjüch,
   Un ok eenmal up'n Buss- un Beeddag,
   Dor see de Kerl, den kennt wi nich.
   He harr sik aber böös verrekent,
   De Lüüd de seed'n, wie arbeit nich.
   Dar schraal de Wind ok noch 5 Streeken,
   Wat weer de Kerl dunn gnatterich.

MAGELLAN

1. There was an antique rotten hulk once,
   A clipper ship named *Magellan.*
   There was no time to brace in daytime,
   Only at night the job was done.
   (Repeat fourth line in each verse)
   No matter how strong the gales were blowin',
   Nothing was done during the day,
   But when the bell struck: "Knock off work, boys!"
   To stretch and haul we had to stay.
   Ch.: Sing' valle ralle, ralle ralle rala, rala, rala!
         Sing' valle ralle, ralle ralle rala,
         Valleri, valleri, vallera!

2. This was the way the skipper tricked us,
   He liked this well and thought 'twas smart,
   And when you'd just sat down for supper,
   He roared: "All hands to the royal halyards!"
   This order nightlong he kept saying,
   We rushed to bowlines, sheets, and brace,
   We heaved and hauled and kept on stretching,
   We gained no inch, but a sweating face!

3. And on Good Friday he would tell us,
   "This is no holiday for you!"
   We had the stinkin' workday's pea soup,
   Too much, was this, for the *Magellan*'s crew.
   We told the skipper: "Nothin' doin'!
   No work today, we sing and dance!"
   And then the wind shifted against us,
   You should have seen the Old Man's glance.

SAILORS' FOOD AND DRINK

Food in ships under sail, from early times right up to the Second World War, was pretty rough. In the ships of the Norsemen and the cogs of Bremen men lived on smoked meat, salt fish, hard-baked rye bread, rank cheese and butter, nuts, mead, and ale. An English sailor's diet in the early years of the seventeenth century wasn't much better. For four "meat days" a sailor got a pound of biscuit, a gallon of beer, and two pounds of beef, with salt; or alternatively a pound of bacon or pork and a pint of peas. For the three so-called Banyan days – Wednesday, Thursday, and Friday – he received a quarter pound of stockfish (dried salt cod), a quarter pound of butter, and the same ration of cheese. Three hundred years later a seaman's grub was much the same: salt beef or pork and "hard tack" or Liverpool pantiles (biscuits) – full of maggots and weevils – being the standard daily

food. French *matelots* (as well as Spanish and Portuguese *marineros*) reveled in their *bacalhao* or salt cod, and such bread as they had rejoiced in the descriptive name of *calliorne* – the name of a wooden pulley-block!

Most Latin seamen probably dined better than Northern ones owing to the skillful use of sardines and anchovies, onions, macaroni, and beans. Beans, incidentally, were a notable item in the diet of German *Matrosen*. In British and American ships young seamen turned out all sorts of concoctions ("manavalins") made mainly from chunks of salt meat and biscuits, having the queer names of "dandyfunk," "dogsbody," "crackerhash," and "skillagalee." Fanny Adams, the name English sailors gave to tinned beef, was a young girl murdered by Frederick Baker, a solicitor's clerk, in a Hampshire village in 1867. In 1874 a girl called Harriet Lane was

murdered by Henry Wainright, a brushmaker, in Whitechapel, London. He was caught and hung at Newgate in 1875. The seven-pound tins of mutton supplied at that time to merchant ships got the name of Harriet Lane from seamen soon after.

An interesting description of a sailor (suitable at any period) is given in a rare book of 1631, *A Strappado for the Devil* by Richard Braithwaite: "The sea cannot roar abroad than hee within, fire him but with liquor. He is watchful as a crane in a storme and as secure as a dormouse in a calme....he can sleepe as well on a sack of pumice as a pillow of doune. He can spin up a rope like a spider and down again like lightning. The rope is his road and the topmast his beacon. He hath an invincible stomach, which ostridge-like could well-neare digest iron."

Sailor drink throughout the ages covers every type of alcohol as well as, in later years, coffee and tea. Barnaby Slush (*Naval Royal*, 1709) describes a "brandy-cask" thus: "Liquor is the very cement that keeps the mariner's body together." Latin seamen, of course, had their *vino* but it was the English Jack Tar who drank the strangest of concoctions in the sixteenth, seventeenth, and eighteenth centuries: Arrack, Poor John (mentioned by the diarist Pepys), Blackstrap (named for a bay near Gibraltar), Miss Taylor (Mistela), Pandoodle, Scratch-platter, Sir Cloudesley (after a British Admiral), Rosalie, Swipes (watered beer), Bumbo (rum, sugar, water, and nutmeg), Flip (beer, spirit, and sugar), and of course grog (watered rum).

SUPEN UT, EN DRAM PÅ MAN

NORWEGIAN-SWEDISH: CAPSTAN SONG

This capstan song, referring to the delights of brandy, is from the recollection of an old sailmaker, Oskar Johansson of Masthugger in Gothenburg, who identified the words as a sort of Norwegian-Swedish. Strangely enough he called the shanty "Oyez, Oyez" – the words used by an English town crier – and the worldwide use of the English expression for sailors in general – Johnnies – crops up in his song.

Å su-pen ut, en dram på man! Väl klar-ar sku-tan sig från land, Om blott I hug-ger i med kläm, En dram för oss John-nies! Kom hör, kom hör, kom hör oss nu! Ur dju-pa stru-par kal-las du, En tår som går från lår till lår, En dram för oss John-nies!

SINK IT DOWN, A TOT EACH MAN

2. Du stewart, fram med flaska grann!
Fyll i en peg till varje man!
De ä långt till Rio som ni vet.

3. Slå pall i spelet, vinda hem!
Nu går det med en väldans kläm,
Slik olja nyttar som i ser.

4. Den stewart kommer snart igen,
Så fort vårt ankar vindats hem.
Ligg an på spaken, alle man!

5. Fast heaven, gubbar, klart vid fall!
Nu alla segel sättas skall,
Stolt skutan faller av för vind.

1. Oh, sink it down, a tot each man,
Oh, soon the ship will clear the land,
If ye heave strong and bear a hand,
Ch.: A good tot for us Johnnies!
Full ch.: Oh, listen, listen, hear us now,
Out of deep throats we're
[calling you,
A tot which goes from man
[to man,
A tot for us Johnnies!

2. Ho, steward, bring the bottle-O,
Pour out a tot – four fingers, so,
The way to Rio's long, ye know,

3. The caps'n pawls are clankin' slow,
But now we heave more lively-O,
Such "oil" is useful, as you know!

4. The steward soon will bring more rum,
As soon as we've made one more run,
Breast high the bars now, every son!

5. 'Vast heavin', bullies, clear the fall,
New on the stays'l halyard haul,
The bark now from the wind does fall.

DES SEEMANNS TRINKLIED

GERMAN: FOREBITTER

In Germany, *Trinklieds* are as common among landlubbers as they are among seamen; soldiers, students, farmers, and so on each have their own special drinking songs. The translator of this seaman's drinking ditty, in order to keep to a rhyme, has at times given a rather free rendering of the original: a west wind, for example, instead of a nor'easter. In the third verse the firemen down below, in the sweltering stokeholds of the old coal-burning steamers, are not forgotten, for they too got extremely thirsty and a "tot" helped them to shovel the coal into the hungry fires "twice as fast," although usually (in my day) oatmeal-water was the liquid they imbibed while working.

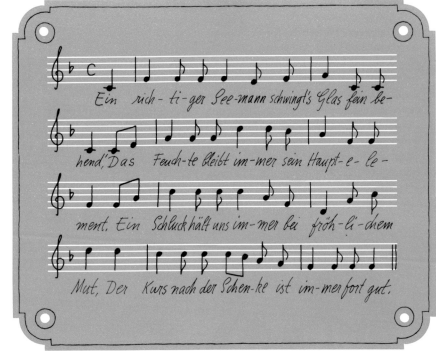

Ein rich-ti-ger See-mann schwingt's Glas fein be-
hend', Das Feuch-te bleibt im-mer sein Haupt-e-le-
ment. Ein Schluck hält uns im-mer bei fröh-li-chem
Mut, Der Kurs nach der Schen-ke ist im-mer fort gut.

2. Tiefnächtlich auf Posten kann's öfter wohl sein,
   Da pfeift uns der Nord-Ost durch Mark und durch Bein,
   Und stürmt er mit Hagel und Schneewirbel rauf,
   Dann taut nur der Grog uns den Lebensgeist auf.

3. Und die vor dem Feuer im Kesselraum stehn,
   Mocht oftmals vor Hitze das Denken vergehn,
   Gibts da ein gut Tröpflein, wirds Auge gleich hell,
   Dann schippt sich die Kohle noch einmal so schnell.

4. Und sind wir im Hafen, dann gehn wir an Land,
   Und schaun wo ein Wirtshaus nicht weit liegt vom Strand,
   Drin werfen wir Anker am Fässchen gar bald,
   Und trinken und singen, dass alles so schallt.

SAILOR'S DRINKING SONG

1. A real sailor can elbow his glass,
   He loves both the sea and the wine,
   A nip gives him courage and happiness,
   There is always a pub suits him fine.

2. At night, at the wheel, aloft, or on deck,
   A hailstorm may blow from the west,
   He knows that a grog at the end of the watch,
   Warms him up, is of all things the best.

3. And those down below, in oil, sweat, and steam,
   In the heat, forget almost to think,
   But their eyes start to shine and they move twice as fast,
   When you tell them there's something to drink.

4. And when we're ashore, our port is the pub,
   To moor there, nothing else is our aim,
   Our anchor gets hold near the beer and the bar,
   And to drink and to sing is the game.

DRUNKEN SAILOR

ENGLISH: STAMP 'N' GO SONG

Although nowadays very well known, this shanty was only used in ships with very large crews, when it was possible to grasp a halyard and stamp away up the deck, the sail steadily ascending the mast, with all hands roaring out the song in unison. It is one of the oldest known Anglo-Saxon shanties, having been sung in the Indiamen of the Honorable John Company. It appears with music in *Incidents of a Whailing Voyage* (1839) by Olmstead. The tune is from a traditional Irish air.

'Way, hay, an'up she ris-es! Pat-ent blocks o' diff'rent siz-es, 'Way, hay, an'up she ris-es! Ear-lye in the morn-in'! What shall we do wi' a drunk-en sail-or? What shall we do wi' a drunk-en sail-or? What shall we do wi' a drunk-en sail-or? Ear-lye in the morn-in'!

It was one of the very few work songs permitted in the smaller ships of the "King's Navee." In merchant ships of later years, with small crews, its usage was confined to the job of going "'bout ship" when the braces would be manned and stamped away with, or when hoisting light sails hand-over-hand; in this latter chore only the chorus would be sung. The word "early" was usually sung "ear-lye" – the pronunciation "eye" for "ee" being traditional also among shore singers of English folksongs.

2. Put him in the long-boat, till he gets sober.

3. Keep him there an' make him bale her.

4. Trice him up in a runnin' bowline.

5. Tie him to the taffrail when she's yard-arm under.

6. Put him in the scuppers with a hose-pipe on him.

7. Take him, an' shake him, an' try an' wake him.

8. What'll we do with a Limejuice skipper?

9. Soak him in oil till he sprouts a flipper.

10. Scrape the hair off his chest with a hoop-iron razor.

11. What shall we do with a drunken soldier?

12. Put him in the burrack-room till he gets sober.

BILLY BOY

ENGLISH: WINDLASS AND CAPSTAN

This is another sea ditty which emanated from shore folksong. Terry, the English sea shanty collector from Tyneside, gives the sailor version as Northumbrian, but there were variants from many other parts of Britain.

The final lines of all shore versions have (usually as chorus):

Because she was a young thing,
An' lately left her mammy-O!

or:

Because she was too young,
For to leave her mammy.

The timber-droghers, too, had a version for stowing timber through the square bow-ports of such ships, a version which ties up with both "Billy Boy" and the "Left her mammy-O" versions. This was called "My Bonnie Hieland Lassie." There is also an American hillbilly variant called "Willie Can She Cook?" "Billy Boy" was one of the very few shanties in which, at times, two shantymen would be employed, one asking the questions, the other singing the answers.

Where have ye bin all the day, Bil-ly Boy, Bil-ly Boy? Where have ye bin all the day, me Bil-ly Bo-y? I've bin walk-in' on the quay with me charm-in' Nan-cy Lee. An' sweet Nan-cy tick-l'd me fan-cy, oh, me charm-in' Bil-ly Boy!

2. Is she fit to be yer wife, Billy Boy, Billy Boy?
Aye, she's fit to be me wife as the fork is to the knife.

3. Can she cook a bit o' steak, Billy Boy, Billy Boy?
She can cook a bit o' steak, aye, an' make a griddle cake.

4. Can she make an Irish stew, Billy Boy, Billy Boy?
She can make an Irish stew, aye, an' singin' hinnies, too.

5. Does she sleep right close to thee, Billy Boy, Billy Boy?
Aye, she sleeps quite close to me, like the bark is to the tree.

6. Can she make a feather bed, Billy Boy, Billy Boy?
She can make a feather bed firm for any sailor's head.

7. Will she ever let yer go, Billy Boy, Billy Boy?
No, she'll never let me go, for she's mine from truck to toe.

IK KWAM LAST OVER EEN BERG

DUTCH: CAPSTAN SONG

There is not much to say about this drinking-cum-capstan song. It is in a folksong style common enough ashore, in which the last important word is left out, keeping the listener guessing until the last line, which supplies the missing word or phrase.

I believe this comes from Terschilling, as do most Dutch seasongs. Knowing Dutch seamen I'm surprised that wine *(wijn)* is mentioned, since bols or "squareface" gin was the alcohol most favored by them.

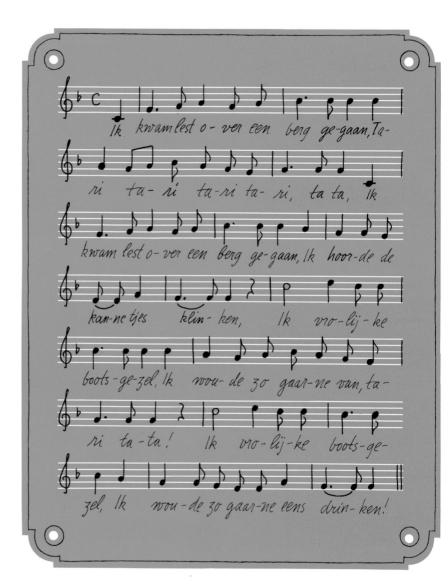

2. Heer waard, tap mij ene kan met wijn,
   Tari tari tari tari, ta ta,
   Die kanne was scheef van onderen,
   Ik vrolijke bootsgezel,
   Ik gooide hem dat 't, tari ta ta,
   Ik vrolijke bootsgezel,
   Ik gooide hem, dat 't donderde.

3. En toen het wijntje geschonken was,
   Tari tari tari tari, ta ta,
   Die waard wou er mij niet borgen,
   Ik vrolijke bootsgezel,
   Ik had er geen geldje voor, tari ta ta,
   Ik vrolijke bootsgezel,
   Ik had er geen geldje voor morgen.

4. Zij trokken mij daar mijne kleren uit,
   Tari tari tari tari, ta ta,
   Zij brachten mij in ene schure,
   Ik vrolijke bootsgezel,
   Ik hon er van koude niet, tari ta ta,
   Ik vrolijke bootsgezel,
   Ik hon er van koude niet duren.

5. En toen ik daar in die schure lag,
   Tari tari tari tari, ta ta,
   Wel, raad eens, wat ik er dachte,
   Ik vrolijke bootsgezel,
   Had ik nu de waard zijne, tari ta ta,
   Ik vrolijke bootsgezel,
   Had ik nu de waard zijne dochter.

6. Toen ik de waard zijne dochter had,
   Tari tari tari tari, ta ta,
   Wat gaf zij er mij ten lone,
   Ik vrolijke bootsgezel,
   Kreeg twee schone goudene, tari ta ta,
   Ik vrolijke bootsgezel,
   Kreeg twee schone goudene kronen.

LAST TIME
I CROSSED THE HILL

1. Last time I crossed the hill,
   Tari tari tari tari, ta ta,
   (Repeat first line in each verse)
   I heard the jugs a-ringing,
   I, a merry boatman,
   I should like to tari ta ta,
   I, a merry boatman,
   I should like to drink.

2. Landlord sell me a jug of wine,
   Tari tari tari tari, ta ta,
   The jug was cracked at the bottom,
   I, a merry boatman,
   I threw it, so that it tari ta ta,
   I, a merry boatman,
   I threw it, so that it splintered.

3. And when I'd had me wine,
   Tari tari tari tari, ta ta,
   That landlord wouldn't let me go,
   I, a merry boatman,
   I hadn't any money for tari ta ta,
   I, a merry boatman,
   I hadn't any money for to pay.

4. They then stripped me naked,
   Tari tari tari tari, ta ta,
   They threw me into the barn,
   I, a merry boatman,
   There from cold I couldn't tari ta ta,
   I, a merry boatman,
   There from cold I couldn't last.

5. And as I lay there in that barn,
   Tari tari tari tari, ta ta,
   'Twas then that I thought,
   I, a merry boatman,
   If I now got the landlord's tari ta ta,
   I, a merry boatman,
   If I now got the landlord's daughter.

6. When I'd had the landlord's daughter,
   Tari tari tari tari, ta ta,
   How d'yer think she paid me?
   I, a merry boatman,
   She gave me two nice golden tari ta ta,
   I, a merry boatman,
   She gave me two nice golden crowns.

BESANSCHOOT AN

GERMAN-PLATTDEUTSCH: FOREBITTER

Although my friend and translator disagrees with the direct translation of *"Besanschoot an!"* as "Mizen sheet!" (spanker sheet), this is what I always believed it to be when under sail in German ships. Like the English "Splice the main brace!" it had the meaning of "Rum (or schnapps) for the watch." The Norwegian sailor spoke of *mesan skjot* and the Swedes called this doling out of strong drink "Letting the lark out of its cage" *(Slipp nu Laerkin ut av buret)* – although Scandinavians also used *Storbrassen splitsas*, a form of the English expression.

2. *Un weer de Anker denn gelicht,*
   Cuxhaben eerst passeert,
   Un keem denn Helgoland in Sicht,
   Denn güng jo nicks verkeert,
   Un weer denn eerst de Wach upsteckt,
   Denn röppt de Stüürmann:
   To Koje, wer de Wach nich hett,
   Aber eerst: "Besanschoot an!"

3. *Un in'n Kanal bi Westen Wind,*
   Hett dat Krüzen gor keen Enn,
   Dor heet dat denn recht oft geswind,
   Purr up de Wach tom Wenn'n,
   Un weer dat Wenden denn gedaan,
   Denn keem de Kock heran,
   Mit'n groten Buddel unnern Arm,
   Un grööl: "Besanschoot an!"

HERE'S YOUR RUM!

1. For many months, for many years, we've sailed the salty seas,
   But never lost on nights of storm our guts and bravery,
   We love the run of salty foam, the rolling waves that come,
   But we like best the captain's roar:
   "Come on, here is your rum!"
   (Repeat last two lines in each verse as chorus)

2. The anchor's up, the canvas loose, past Cuxhaven then we sail,
   With Heligoland soon left behind, we pray for a steady gale,
   "One man on lookout, relieve the wheel!" the first mate's orders come:
   "Free watch below!" and then his words?
   "Come aft an' get yer rum!"

3. But at Cape Horn in western storms our tops'ls blew away,
   "All hands on deck! Put her about!" 'Twas such all night an' day,
   At last the hardships had an end, we saw our steward come,
   He called, a bottle in his hand,
   "Come aft an' get yer rum!"

DE KOCK

GERMAN-PLATTDEUTSCH:
CAPSTAN AND HALYARD SHANTY

This shanty is sung to the tune of a once well known shore song, "In Berlin Sagt 'Er." When hauling on the halyards the pull came on the words *"Seggt he!"* In all versions the story is humorous and depicts the position of the cook in sailing ships as a man isolated from the rest of the crew, knowing full well that everyone depends on his skills or lack of them. He guards his galley against intruders, using a meat-cleaver if need be.

Juch-hei lust-ig, Seggt he, Ich bün Kock, Seggt he,
Drink ok geern, Seggt he, Een Glas Grog,
CH. Seggt he, Fohr to See, Seggt he, Twin-dig Jahrn,
Seggt he, Hewwok üm-mer, Seggt he, Glück-lich fahr'n.

The only seamanlike job he did was to slack the foresheet in "goin' 'bout ship," this rope being near his galley door. Hence one of his names was "Lord of the Foresheet" (German: *Hein Fockschoot*). In most German and Scandinavian ships he was given the English nickname of "Doc" or "Doctor." All his nicknames in North European sailing ships were connected with grease, dirt, or soot: *Smutje, Smuddjẻ, Smeerdraak, Smutt, Kokke-fa'n* (Danish), *Kesselkommandant, Kokkesmörja* (Norwegian).

2. *Gäale Arften,*
Kaak ik moor,
Röör se ummer,
Düchtig dor,
Een Stück Speck,
Tämlick groot,
Smeckt up See,
Wurlich good.

3. *Back ik Kluten,*
As bekannt,
Spee ik eerst,
In die Hand,
Maak se denn,
Kugelrund,
Smecken good,
Sund gesund.

4. *Doch een Deel,*
Ist dorbi,
Dat ik sorg,
Of för mi,
For mien Mo,
For mien Fliet,
Stäk ik wat,
An de Siet.

THE COOK

1. Hurrah jolly,
   Ch.: Sez he,
   I am cook,
   Ch.: Sez he,
   Drink right well,
   Ch.: Sez he,
   A glass of grog,
   Ch.: Sez he,
   Been to sea,
   Ch.: Sez he,
   Twenty years,
   Ch.: Sez he,
   And have always,
   Ch.: Sez he,
   Plenty luck.

2. Yellow peas,
   Cook for me,
   Keep them stirred,
   Right way through,
   A piece of bacon,
   Jolly big,
   Taste and see,
   Mighty good.

3. Baked dumplings,
   As well known,
   I split first,
   In the hand,
   Then I roll 'em,
   Make 'em round,
   They taste well,
   And are sound.

4. But one part,
   That is there,
   I take care,
   For myself,
   For my worry,
   And for my trouble,
   Always something,
   Put aside.

LIMEJUICE SHIP

ENGLISH: FOREBITTER

In 1845, in the British merchant service, a code governing food, punishments, and so on was promulgated. Of course many years earlier a code did exist, that of *Oleron*, known among all northern seafaring nations, but from those days onward there was a gap in suitable rules governing the daily life of a seafarer. This 1845 ruling was again enlarged in 1894 and a rider introduced containing an anti-scurvy clause, declaring that limejuice was to be served out to each seaman after ten days at sea. It was from this Merchant Shipping Act – known as the Limejuice Act – that British sailors were given the name of Limejuicers, and later Limeys, by the Americans. British seamen, naturally, soon turned out this sarcastic forebitter poking fun at the Act.

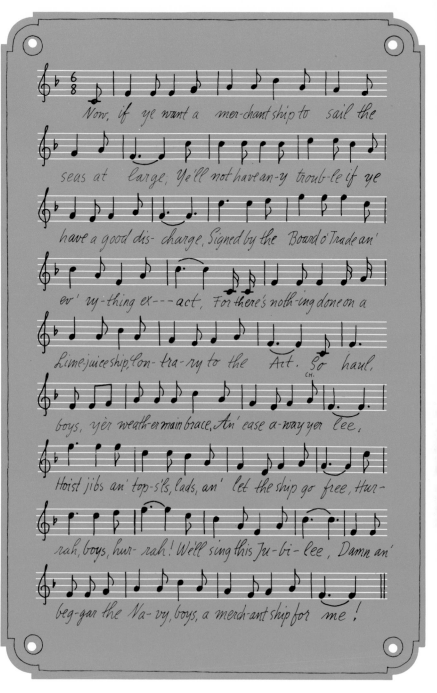

Now, if ye want a merchant ship to sail the seas at large, Ye'll not have any trouble if ye have a good discharge, Signed by the Board o' Trade an' ev'rything ex---act, For there's nothing done on a Limejuice ship, Contrary to the Act. So haul, boys, yer weather mainbrace, An' ease away yer lee, Hoist jibs an' top-s'ls, lads, an' let the ship go free, Hurrah, boys, hurrah! We'll sing this Jubilee, Damn an' beggar the Navy, boys, a merchant ship for me!

2. Now, when ye join a merchant ship ye'll hear yer Articles read,
They'll tell ye of yer beef an' pork, yer butter an' yer bread,
Yer sugar, tea, an' coffee, boys, yer peas an' beans exact,
Yer limejuice an' vinegar, boys, according to the Act.

3. No watch an' watch the first day out, according to the Act,
Ten days out we all lay aft to get our limejuice whack,
Fetch out the handy-billy, boys, an' clap it on the tack,
For we're gonna set that mains'l, oh, accordin' to the Act.

4. It's up the deck, me bully boys, wid many a curse we go,
Awaitin' to hear eight bells struck that we may go below,
The watch is called, eight bells is struck, an' the log is hove exact,
Relieve the wheel an' go below, according to the Act.

DER ALLERBESTE KOCH

GERMAN: FOREBITTER

This is a song similar in content to "De Kock" and its tune is a rather well known one from shoreside – a great favorite among German students. I took part in the singing of this lively song many times in the 1920s, learning it from a young Frisian Islands seaman whose father was master in one of Laiesz's Cape-Horners earlier in this century. The sentiments given in the last verse reflect a universal belief among seamen that most cooks and stewards "cut down" so much on the sailors' grub that by the time they retired they owned rows of houses built on the illicit proceeds gained from starving poor sailors.

2. *Des Morgens, wenn ich früh aufsteh,*
   Koch' ich der Mannschaft gleich Kaffee,
   Zu stark, da ist er nicht gesund,
   Man nimmt ja'n Priemje in den Mund.

3. *Die Töpfe halt' ich immer rein,*
   Von innen und von aussen fein,
   Ich spül' sie alle Monat' aus,
   Das ist bei uns auf See so Brauch.

4. *Das Essen für den Kapitän,*
   Schmeckt kräftig und recht angenehm,
   D'rum wird davon, eh' es serviert,
   Das beste an die Seit' plaziert.

5. *Für Schmalz, da kriegt man schönes Geld,*
   Still wird es an die Kant' gestellt,
   Und ist die Reise dann vollbracht,
   Wird Schmalz und Speck zu Geld gemacht.

THE FINEST COOK

1. I am the very finest cook,
   Ch.: Jub hei di! Jub hei da!
   The saucepan's leak with chewin' plug,
   Ch.: Jub hei di, hei da!
   I stopped so well, and made it shine,
   The soup it tasted ever so fine.
   Full ch.: Jub hei di! Jub hei da!
       Schnapps is good for the cholera!
       Jub hei di! Jub hei da!
       Jub hei di, hei da!

2. Each morn when I rise early too,
   I then make coffee for the crew,
   It's weak and very good for you,
   But never drink when you baccy chew!

3. The pots I keep quite clean and fine,
   Both inside and the outside shine,
   Each month I wash 'em out and so,
   In the briny sea I rinse 'em, ho!

4. The captain's food that I do make,
   Is really fine and nice to take,
   And so I purloin all the best,
   And place it aside in me old sea-chest.

5. For lard a chap can get good cash,
   So I keep it far from meat and hash,
   For this trip must make me rich,
   With lard and bacon to do the trick!

WHISKEY JOHNNY

AMERICAN/ENGLISH: HALYARD SHANTY

One should never be too dogmatic about the type of job to which a certain shanty should be allocated. Old sailors have often pointed out that in certain ships a so-called halyard shanty has been used at the capstan, while in other ships the reverse was the situation. This halyard shanty, according to written record as well as information given by ancient mariners, was often sung at the windlass brakes.

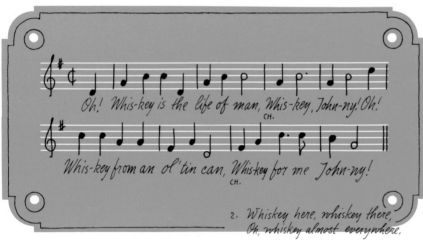

Oh! Whis-key is the life of man, Whis-key, John-ny! Oh!
CH.
Whis-key from an ol' tin can, Whiskey for me John-ny!
CH.

2. Whiskey here, whiskey there,
   Oh, whiskey almost everywhere.

A native of the Welsh village of Aberdovey once told me that this song was voiced by lifeboatmen as they hove the local sailing lifeboat up the ship, by means of a portable capstan.

As recent as last year, in the Tall Ships' Race, I discovered that four-line halyard shanties worked well on a brake windlass. But "Whiskey Johnny" was normally sung, in a full-rigged ship, at the mizen t'gallant halyards, hoping that the plea for whiskey from the men would reach the ears of the master standing in close proximity on his poop. Why a song about whiskey became so popular among rum-sodden mariners is difficult to explain!

3. Whiskey up an' whiskey down,
   Whiskey all around the town.

4. I'll drink it hot, I'll drink it cold,
   I'll drink it new, I'll drink it old.

5. Whiskey killed me poor ol' dad,
   Whiskey drove me mother mad.

6. I had a sister, her name wuz Lize,
   She puts whiskey in her pies.

7. Whiskey made me pawn me clothes,
   Whiskey gave me this red nose.

8. My wife an' I do not agree,
   She puts whiskey in her tea.

9. Some likes whiskey, some likes beer,
   I wisht I had a barrel here.

10. Oh, the mate likes whiskey, the skipper likes rum,
    The sailors like both, but we can't git none.

11. Oh, a tot of whiskey for each man,
    An' a bloody big bottle for the shantyman.

12. If whiskey wuz a river an' I wuz a duck,
    I'd dive to the bottom an' niver come up.

13. If whiskey wuz a river an' I could swim,
    I'd say here goes an' dive right in.

14. I wisht I knew where whiskey grew,
    I'd eat the leaves an' the branches, too.

15. There wuz a Limejuice skipper of the name of Hogg,
    Once tried to stop his sailors' grog.

16. Which made the helmsman so weak an' slack,
    That the helmsman caught her flat aback.

17. An' ever after so they say,
    That crew got grog three times a day.

18. So we'll boost her up an' bowl along,
    An' drink that skipper's health in song.

19. Now, if ye ever go to Frisco town,
    Mind you steer clear of Shanghai Brown.

20. He'll dope yer whiskey night an' morn,
    An' then shanghai yiz round Cape Horn.

21. Two months' wages they are dead,
    An' a donkey's breakfast for yer bed.

22. Ol' Shanghai Brown an' Larry Marr,
    Their names are known both near an' far.

23. Oh, whiskey is the life o' man,
    It always wuz since time began.

24. I thought I heard the Old Man say,
    Give one more pull, lads, then belay!

SUPERSTITIONS, CUSTOMS AND PIDGIN

Sailors have always been superstitious, thanks to the nature of their calling. In ancient times beliefs in sea monsters such as sea serpents, kraken, Jenny Hanivers, the Bishop Fish (which would rise up above a ship, bless the crew in Latin, and then devour them), sirens, mermaids, and so on may have been fostered by Phoenician seamen (the first through the Straits of Gibraltar) in order to keep the lucrative tin coast of Cornwall as their own preserve. The names of certain animals – mainly those considered witches' familiars, such as the cat, rabbit, hare, goat, and so on – were never used at sea, made-up names being used instead. If a seaman or fisherman met a black cat, priest, or nun on the way to his ship, it was considered bad luck and he would return home. Sailing on a Friday, especially the thirteenth, was very "bad joss," based on the biblical Good Friday and the thirteen diners at the Last Supper, although Columbus himself sailed on a Friday, reached America on a Friday, and returned home on a Friday.

Russian Finns were considered to be good "whistler-uppers" of the wind, and sailors in Sweden believed that a certain king, Eric Windy-Cap (Eric VI) of the tenth century, could conjure up the wind by turning his peak to the desired quarter. In classical times a dead kingfisher would be hung up, the direction of its beak forecasting the direction from which the wind would come; sailing-ship men would use a dried flying fish to get the same results.

The modern saluting of the quarterdeck comes from the days of the Latin circumnavigators when a statue of the Virgin Mary adorned the poop and genuflections were made in her direction by the crew.

Incidentally, the word "poop" comes from the Latin *pupis*, a doll, and relates to the fact that in this part of the ship the image (or doll) of the Virgin was erected.

The international custom among seamen of the Crossing of the Line probably had its origin in the paying of wine tributes to gods of certain headlands in the Mediterranean. At one time a Moorish marabout on the African side of the Straits of Gibraltar would demand wine libations from ships passing through. Off the Burlings (Portugal) and at the Tropics of Cancer and Capricorn early Latin navigators would appease the sea demons by certain rituals, and whalemen entering the Arctic would perform a ceremony on crossing the Arctic Circle.

The first mention of Father Neptune boarding a ship at the equator appears in William Richardson's *Journal* of 1791. The full ritual of shaving initiates and ducking them, with the accompanying rough play, died out in sail before the end of the last century.

It is difficult to say when (or where) Pidgin English was originally invented (if that's the word), but it reached its perfection in the Black Islands of Melanesia. Examples are: "Whitey man him fighten hands b'long him, box him sing out plenty," meaning "a man playing a piano"; "Big fish kai-kai along you flenty" for "a shark will eat you"; "One-legged white-fella Mary" is a white woman (a hundred years ago natives thought white women, in dresses to their ankles, had only one leg); and a modern bit of pidgin is "Basket blonga teetee, blonga one-legged white-fella Mary," which translates into "a white girl's bra."

DE HOFFNUNG

GERMAN-PLATTDEUTSCH:
HALYARD SHANTY

I learned this hauling song from a
young Hamburg seaman in the twen-
ties. It was popular in all German sailing ships. It has a touch of the German
folk legend *Faust* about it. It would
appear that the skipper in this tale was
a bit overdue on the homeward run.
When Old Nick appears the skipper
offers him his soul if Satan can speed
up the ship a little. When the time
comes for repayment the skipper isn't
so happy. However, the cunning old
carpenter hooks the Devil up to the
anchor, and on dropping the "hook"
the Devil is sent to the bottom of the
sea!

THE *HOFFNUNG*

1. The *Hoffnung* was a hundred days on the go,
   Ch.: To me way hay ho, howday!
   She sailed from Hamburg to Valparaiso,
   Ch.: Oh, a long time ago!

2. *Se seilte goot un se seilte hart,*
   Se harr so'ne gode un kostbare Fracht.

3. *Un as de Ool nu flucht un gnattert,*
   Dor keem de Düvel över de Reeling klattert.

4. *"Wenn mi in tein Dag nen Kanal du bringst,*
   Denn krigst mien Seel, so waar as du stinkst."

5. *De Pott leep negentein Milen toletzt,*
   Dor harr de Düvel de Skyseils bisett.

6. *Un as se nu kemen in'n Kanal to Stell,*
   Dar seggt de Düvel, "Nu her mit de Seel!"

7. *Dar seggt de Ool, "Nu lot di man tiet,*
   Wi goot to Anker bi Cape St. Patrick."

8. *De Düvel de weer vör Freid ganz weg,*
   He leep op de Back, sett den Anker op slip.

9. *De ole Timm'mann harr grote Freid,*
   He harr den Düvel sien'n Steert mitvertäut.

10. *Un as de Anker nu suust an den Grund,*
    Suust de Düvel mit, disse Swienehund.

2. She sailed good and she sailed hard,
   She had such a fine and costly cargo.

3. And as the Old Man swore and cursed,
   The Devil came climbing over the rail.

4. "If you bring me to the Channel in ten days' time,
   Surely as you stink you will get my soul."

5. The old hulk at last went eighteen knots,
   The Devil had the skys'ls set.

6. And when she came to the Channel to anchor,
   Then said the Devil, "Give me your soul."

7. Then said the Old Man, "Take your time,
   We have to anchor by Cape St. Patrick."

8. The Devil was now more than overjoyed,
   He ran up the fo'c'slehead to let go the anchor.

9. The old carpenter was greatly pleased,
   He had spliced the Devil's backside to the anchor.

10. And as the anchor went down to the ground,
    The Devil went with it — the dirty big hound!

THE FLYING DUTCHMAN

ENGLISH: FOREBITTER

The legend of the *Flying Dutchman* has been kept alive by many besides common seamen. Marryat the novelist has given us his version of the phantom ship and then there is the world-famed opera *Der Fliegende Holländer* by Wagner. The simple sailor legend tells of Vanderdecken or Van Straaten, master of a Dutch ship endeavoring to round the Cape of Good Hope in adverse winds. In desperation he swears that "neither God nor devil will stop me rounding this Cape of Storms!" As he utters these words a great voice answers through the roar of the wind: "I am greater than thou. 'Twill profit ye little if ye defy me. For defying me you shall sail these seas alone and forever – except for your cabin boy. He'll attend you, not as a human but as a demon. The food he brings you will be uneatable. From this moment ye will sail until Eternity! I have spoken!"

Instantly the crew and passengers all fade away, leaving Vanderdecken and his demon cabin boy on the poop all alone. Many sailors have vouched for the phantom ship's appearance – always riding head to wind. It is said that Vanderdecken tries to get a sailor to post his letters to his wife, but if one accepts them his death is certain. Terrible storms arise when he is in the offing and a ship's drinking water will turn sour when he is near.

Around the world, there are more of these phantoms – off the coast of Germany sailors have seen Falkenburg, a nobleman, aboard his ghost ship, from the masts of which flames emanate. And off the coasts of Chile the phantom ship of the Caleutes, called the *Caleuche* – a bluff-bowed galleon – is often seen, especially on New Year's Eve when her malevolence is most potent.

It was a wild and stor-my night, far south-ward of the Cape, When from a stiff nor'-west-er we had just made our es-cape; Like a ba-by in its cra-dle, oh, the waves were hush'd to sleep, And peace-ful-ly we sail'd a-long the bo-som of the deep. And peaceful-ly we sail'd a-long the bo-som of the deep.

2. When suddenly the helmsman gave a shout of danger and of fear,
   As if he had seen some sudden danger near,
   He looked around the horizon and there upon our lee,
   We saw the Flying Dutchman come bounding o'er the seas,

3. "Take in yer flyin' canvas!" our watchful captain cried.
   "To you an' your ship's company, great peril doth betide!"
   The billows crested high with foam, all angry doth appear,
   The wind springs up a hurricane now Vanderdecken's near.

4. He sails too well, he goes too quick, to mark his eagle flight,
   And lightning like the Dutchman's stern, will soon pass out of sight,
   And distant ships they shudder at the breeze,
   That sends the Flyin' Dutchman in fury o'er the seas.

5. Now mourn for Vanderdecken, for terrible is his doom,
   The oceans round the stormy Cape shall be his living tomb,
   The Dutchman beats about the Cape-night an' day,
   In vain he tries his oath to keep, by entering Table Bay.

MARRIED TO A MERMAID

ENGLISH: FOREBITTER

Mermaids, merry-maids, or fairmaids have been taken seriously by old salts from time immemorial. Mer*men* were mentioned, by the very ancient mariners, long before mer*maids*. In the imagination of the old Norse seafarers, Eskimos in kayaks could have fostered this belief. Dugongs, manatees, and sea-cows have also been offered as the origin of the mermaid. Columbus is said to have seen mermaids but he later came to the conclusion that they were manatees.

On the west coast of Ireland, the isles of Scotland, the coast of Cornwall, and among Scandinavian seamen and the fishermen of the Shetlands, mermaid stories are the most numerous and most believed in. On the end of a pew in a church in Zennor, Cornwall, is carved the figure of a mermaid complete with comb and glass. She is said to have lured a certain fisherman Matthew Trevella down to the ocean depths and there married him. The carving was set up as a warning to local youth not to have anything to do with the wiles of such creatures!

There wuz a gay young farm-er, who lived on Sals'b'ry Plain, He lov'd a rich knight's daught-er dear, an' she lov'd him a-gain; The knight was so dis-tres-sèd, that they should sweet-hearts be, That he had the farm-er soon pres-sèd, and he whipp'd him off to sea. Sing-in Rule Brit-an-nia! Two tan-ners make a bob, Five make two—an'—six, an' one for his knob!

2. 'Twas on the deep Atlantic midst the equinoctial gales,
The young farmer fell overboard among the sharks and whales;
He disappeared so quickly, headlong down went he,
And he went out of sight, like a streak o' light, to the bottom
of the deep, blue sea.

3. We lowered a boat to find him, we thought to see his corpse,
When up to the top, he came with a shock, and said in a voice so hoarse,
"My shipmates and my messmates, oh, do not weep for me,
For I'm married to a mermaid at the bottom of the deep, blue sea."

THE DEAD HORSE

ENGLISH: CEREMONIAL SHANTY

The ceremony known as "Paying off the Dead Horse" had become a rather anemic affair by the latter days of sail, whereas in the days of the clipper ships and the Australian emigrant ships it was quite a spectacular business. The first month's pay of the sailor, in the form of an advance-note, went into the hands of an unscrupulous crimp, ostensibly to pay for lodgings and a tatty sea-outfit, but in actual fact paid for booze and diseased harlots. So the sailor considered his first month at sea a payless one and just a matter of "working for a dead horse."

Oh, a poor old man came ri-ding by,

An' we say so! An' we hope so! A poor old man came ri-ding by, Oh, poor ol' 'orse!

2. Sez I, "Ol' Man yer 'orse will die,"
Sez I, "Ol' Man yer 'orse will die."

3. For one long month I rode him hard,
For one long month I rode him hard.

4. But now yer month is up, ol' Turk,
Git up, yer swine, an' look for work.

5. Git up, yer swine, an' look for graft,
While we lays on an' yanks ye aft.

6. He's as dead as a nail in the lamproom door,
He won't come a-hazin' us no more.

7. We'll use the hair of his tail to sew our sails,
We'll use the hair of his tail to sew our sails.

8. We'll hoist him up to the main yardarm,
We'll hoist him up to the main yardarm.

9. An' drop him down to the depths of the sea,
An' drop him down to the bottom of the sea,

10. We'll sink him down with a long, long roll,
Where the sharks'll have his bottom, an' the
devil have his soul.

In the second dog-watch (6–8 p.m.) on the evening before the first day of the second month – i.e., just before they started working for "real money" – a canvas image of a horse with a rope-yarn mane and tail, stuffed with shavings and some holystones for weight, would be hoisted to the main yardarm to the singing of this shanty. In earlier days a regular procession would take place along the deck, the "horse" surmounted on a gun-carriage, and at the break of the poop the master would await the seamen haulers and give them a tot of rum. When the "horse" reached the yardarm a blue flare would be fired and at the same time a seaman on the yard would cut the gantline dropping the "horse" into the "drink." This shanty was one of the very few working songs used as a ceremonial song, nevertheless it was also used during the voyage for hauling on halyards and other lines.

SAMOA SONG

SAMOAN-PIDGIN: FAREWELL SONG

This is a type of goodbye song that used to be heard throughout the fascinating isles of Polynesia, sung by natives and whites alike on the departure of a ship – a big sailing ship, an inter-Island trading schooner, or a steamer. It is in the mixed language known as Samoan-Pidgin. The word "pidgin" is a native form of the word "business," used from the China Coast to Easter Island, and when linked with the name of another language – such as Pidgin-English, Pidgin-German, and so on – indicates a type of trading lingo developed during the years of barter between natives and white merchants and sailors.

Good-bye, my fe-le-ni, o le a ou te-a,
Ae fo-lau le vaa, o le Alii pule me-le-te, Nei galo mai A-pi-a, si ota e-le e-le, Ae maga-tu-a maipea, le au pa-se-se.
Oh, I ne-ver will for-get-- you, Sa-mo-a ele e-le ga-loa-tu, Oh, I ne-ver will for-get--- you, Sa-mo-a e-le-a-tu.

The Samoan or Navigators Group, owned for many years by Germany, was naturally a port-o'-call – Apia being the main port – for German sailing ships and steamers. This song was known entirely or in part by many German seamen engaged in the South Sea trade. The chorus was often sung in German thus:

Oh, ich werde dich ni vergessen,
Samoa vergesse ich nie. (Twice)

2. *Faa foga foga, mai Samoa uma,*
Sai fai atu, o lau faa tusa, pei o le sulu saga,
I totonu o maga, faapea lau pele,
Mai taupou uma.

186

KINAKUSTEN

A SEAMAN'S SONG FROM THE CHINA COAST

PIDGIN-ENGLISH-SWEDISH:
HAULING SHANTY

This Pidgin-English song was extremely popular with Scandinavian sailors on the China Coast in the late nineteenth century. Many of the words thought by Westerners to be Chinese go back to the days of the early Portuguese and Spanish missionaries and traders of the fifteenth and sixteenth centuries.

Från Can-ton till Ma-ca-o, Från Hong-Kong å Lu-li-ao, The sod-gers and sa-i-lors de sjung-it hen-nes love. För ding-e, ding-e ding-dong, hm-di, hm-di! Hon var en sam-pan gir-lie allt i-från Hong-ki-kong.

2. A you-oo like me-hee,
   A mandarin's daughter?
   You sodgers and sailors,
   Som seglar på Hong Kong.

3. I no-o like you-hu,
   You no-o like me-hee,
   You all belong to sodgers,
   You no belong to me.

For instance, the word "junk" for a native boat is the Portuguese word *junco;* "mandarin" for a local judge is from the Spanish *mandar,* to give; "compradore," from *comprar,* to buy; and "pagoda" comes from a corruption of the Sanskrit word *dagoba.* Many pidgin words, such as "bobbery" for foolish talk (Spanish: *boboria*), "can-do," and "maskie" (okay), are still to be heard in the East even today. The odd Swedish word in this song hardly needs translating.

MEIN VADER VOS EIN DUTCHMAN

MY FATHER WAS A DUTCHMAN

PIDGIN-DUTCH: FOREBITTER

The old-time sailing ship Johnny was very partial to "furrin lingoes" but somewhat inadequate when he tried to use them. This song is a rather humorous attempt at Dutch, or perhaps German. A "Dutchman" in the lingo of the old-time sailorman was any member of the Nordic race *except* a Hollander, who was called "Holland Dutch." The general term "Squarehead" was used for all Germans, Scandinavians, and seamen from the Low Countries.

Mein va-der vos ein Dutch-man, Mit mein yaw-
yaw, yaw! Mein va-der vos ein Dutch-man, Mit mein yaw-
yaw, yaw! Mein va-der vos ein Dutch-man, Und mein mut-ter
vos ein Prus-sian, Mit mein yaw, yaw, yaw!

2. Ich spoke ein funny lingo,
Ich spoke ein funny lingo,
Gott for dommey, O by Yingo!

3. Mit mein niggerum, buggerum, stinkum,
Vell, ve'll climb upon der steeples,
Und ve'll spit down on de peoples.

4. Und der polis-man, fireman, steepleman,
Dey all climbs upon de steeple,
Und dey laugh do all the peoples.

5. Oh, ven I vos ein sailor,
Vell ve trink up all der whiskey,
Und it makes us feel damn frisky.

6. Ve did all de bawdy houses,
Und ve hitchum up de trousers,
Und ve catchum all der louses.

7. Ve chase all der bretty frauleins,
Und ve chase 'em und ve tease 'em,
Und ve catch 'em und ve kees 'em.

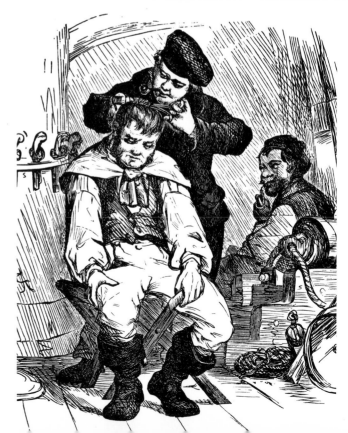

188

SAMPAN GIRL

PIDGIN-ENGLISH: FOREBITTER

This Pidgin-English song comes from both Scandinavian and German seamen in the China Coast trade. It probably originated in the days of the tea clippers when the Canton River and havens up the coast, such as the Golden Pagoda anchorage, Foochow-fu, were chock-a-block with the masts and yards of the clippers loading the precious *cha* (tea).

Me have got a flow-er boat, Come sail-ing Chu-ki-ang.
Sam-pan gir-lie play to you, All the same sing-song.

Although there were other forms of pidgin, none was so ubiquitous as Pidgin-English. In Japan at this time, clipper-ship men and the China hands used a type of pidgin called the Yokohama dialect. It had real Japanese words, no grammar, and the words were linked with short words from other lingoes.

In this song the Chinese words are from the Cantonese dialect. Here are their approximate meanings:

Chu kiang, the Pearl River at Canton
Lao-yeh, master, mister
Tzia-tzia, flower-boat girl, sing-song girl, prostitute
Chi-da, a chicken
Sam-shu, rice or bean wine
Yang-yen, opium
Shang-yen, a cigarette.

2. Lao-yeh, you like me?
   Tzia-tzia, velly good.
   Foreign man to Canton come,
   Me got plenty chow.

3. Homeside have got pidgin,
   Me savvy, me can tell,
   Bring me master chicken,
   Chi-da, velly well.

4. Suppose he likee Sam-shu,
   It all the same can-do,
   Chop-chop me fetch him,
   Big-big Da-bing-yu.

5. You no likee Yang-yen,
   Me lightie littie pipe,
   He go smokie Shang-yen,
   Belong velly velly tight.

PICTURE CREDITS

Barnaby's Picture Library, London: 137;

Bibliothèque Nationale, Paris: 78 (right; Photo Giraudon);

California State Library, Sacramento: 31;

Chicago Historical Society, Chicago: 177 (top);

Cooper-Bridgeman Library, London: 167;

Duval, Bernard: 89;

Elek Publishers, London: 66 (bottom); 90 (bottom);

Giraudon, Paris: 8 (top; Anderson);

Glover, L.: 12 (top);

Heimatmuseum Bremen-Schönebeck, Bremen: 40 (bottom; Photo Evelinde Manon);

Holland Amerika Lijn, Rotterdam: 97 (bottom);

Lehner, Ernst, New York: 180;

The Mansell Collection, London: 15 (bottom right); 18 (bottom left, center and right); 19 (bottom left and right); 26 (center); 26/27 (top); 51 (bottom); 53 (center left); 60 (top); 68 (bottom); 70; 76 (center); 81 (top); 100; 148; 154 (bottom); 162 (bottom); 163 (right); 164 (bottom); 165;

Mariners Museum, Newport News, Va.: 134 (bottom right);

Marinmuseum, Karlskrona: 20 (bottom); 21 (bottom right); 177 (bottom); 188 (bottom);

Mary Evans Picture Library, London: 11 (bottom); 14 (bottom center); 26 (bottom); 28; 33 (top); 35; 39 (bottom); 41; 67 (left); 75 (bottom); 85; 91 (top); 92 (left); 95 (bottom); 101 (top and bottom); 106; 114; 118 (right); 119; 125 (bottom); 136; 145 (center); 147; 153; 154 (center); 155 (bottom); 171 (bottom left); 174 (top); 178;

Metropolitan Museum of Art, New York: 19 (top);

Musée de la Marine, Paris: 38 (bottom right);

Museo di San Martino, Naples: 189 (bottom right);

Museum für Hamburgische Geschichte, Hamburg: 14 (bottom left; Courtesy Elek Publishers); 65 (Photo Nationaal Scheepvaartmuseum, Antwerp); 140 (right);

Mystic Seaport, Inc., USA: 42/43; 72; 124; 142 (bottom);

Nationaal Scheepvaartmuseum, Antwerp: 22; 37 (left); 54 (bottom); 58/59; 60 (center); 87; 103 (right); 161; 173 (bottom);

National Maritime Museum, Greenwich: 9 (center); 14 (bottom right; Courtesy Elek Publishers); 17 (bottom left); 23; 60 (bottom; Courtesy Elek Publishers); 68 (center); 77 (right; Courtesy Elek Publishers); 78 (left); 80 (right); 86; 91 (bottom); 105 (bottom); 107 (center); 122; 159 (bottom); 179 (Courtesy Elek Publishers); 186 (top; Photo Laffont);

Nederlandsch Historisch Scheepvaart Museum, Amsterdam: 15 (bottom center);

The New Brunswick Museum, Saint John, Canada: 24/25;

The New York Historical Society, New York City: 16 (bottom); 30 (bottom);

New York Public Library, New York: 7 (Rare Book Division); 62 (left; Manuscript Division); 126 (top right); 130; 132 (right);

The Peabody Museum, Salem: 34 (right); 57 (bottom right); 73; 94 (left); 144 (bottom center and right); 145 (bottom left, center and right); 151;

Photothèque Laffont, Paris: 141;

Popperfoto, London: 79;

Publisher's Archives: 6; 8 (bottom); 9 (bottom); 10 (bottom); 13; 18 (top); 19 (bottom center); 29; 30 (center); 33 (bottom); 34 (left); 37 (right); 39 (top); 45 (top); 46 (bottom left, center and right); 47; 52 (top); 53 (center right and bottom); 55 (top); 61; 62 (right); 64 (top); 66 (top); 74; 75 (top); 76 (top); 77 (left); 84 (top); 88 (left); 90 (top and center); 92 (right); 95 (top); 96 (left and right); 97 (top); 101 (center); 103 (left); 107 (top and bottom); 109 (top, center and bottom); 110; 115 (top and bottom); 117 (top left and bottom left); 118 (left); 120 (top and bottom); 125 (top); 126 (top left and bottom); 129 (right); 131; 132 (left); 133; 134 (top and bottom left); 135; 138 (top); 142 (top); 146; 149; 150; 152 (top); 154 (top); 155 (top); 159 (top left and right); 162 (top); 163 (left); 164 (top); 171 (top); 173 (top); 175 (top); 176; 182; 184; 185 (top and bottom); 186 (bottom); 187 (left and right); 189 (top);

Radio Times Hulton Picture Library, London: 69; 80 (left); 81 (bottom); 84 (bottom left and right); 152 (bottom); 157 (right); 189 (center);

Roger-Viollet, Paris: 156;

Schiffahrtsmuseum der Oldenburgischen Weserhäfen, Brake: 9 (top);

Shelburne Museum, Shelburne, Vermont, USA: 112/113;

Sjöfartsmuseet, Göteborg: 15 (bottom left);

Statens Sjöhistoriska Museum, Stockholm: 32 (bottom); 82/83; 140 (left); 157 (left); 166; 168 (right);

Victoria and Albert Museum, London: 181;

Wyss, Robert, Adligenswil: 32 (top); 134 (center); 169 (top); 170;

Additional illustrations are reproduced from the following books, with the kind permission of the publishers:

Seafaring America, Alexander Laing (American Heritage, New York, 1974)

Sejlskibe og sømaend i forrige århundrede, Gunnar Knudsen (Chr. Erichsens Forlag, Copenhagen, 1975)

Sozialgeschichte der Frau, Eduard Fuchs (Verlag Neue Kritik KG, Frankfurt, 1973)

The Whale, Leonard Harrison Matthews (George Allen and Unwin, 1968)

Von der Schönheit alter Schiffe, Hans Jürgen Hansen (Gerhard Stalling Verlag, Oldenburg/Hamburg, 1971)

DISCOGRAPHY

The following seasong and shanty records were issued between the 1930s and the 1960s. Many are no longer produced, but the ardent seeker may find the odd one in a secondhand shop. Some, however, have been reissued.

WE'RE ALL BOUND TO GO – Columbia 4689 (Eng.).

SONGS OF THE SEA, Alan Mills and the Shantymen – Folkways FA 2312 (Can.).

SEA SHANTIES, Stanley Slade – HMV BI 0605 (Engl.).

SHANTIES, John Goss and his Cathedral Quartet – HMV, in B series such as B 3782 and B 2940 (Eng.).

THE SINGING SAILOR, A.L. Lloyd and Ewan MacColl – Topic TRL 3 (Eng.).

KNURRHAHN, Kiel-Holtenauer Lotsenchor – Polydor 20263 EPH (Ger.).

AMERICAN SEASONGS AND SHANTIES – Library of Congress AAFS L 26 and AAFS L 27 (Amer.).

PINCH OF SALT, Peter Kennedy, et al. – HMV FOLK (Eng.).

SHANTIES FROM THE SEVEN SEAS, Stan Hugill and York and Albany Crew – HMV CLP 1524 (Eng.).

THE LIVERPOOL PACKET, Stan Kelly – Topic TOP 27 (Eng.).

FAREWELL NANCY – Topic 12 T 110 (Eng.).

A SAILOR'S GARLAND, Ewan MacColl and A.L. Lloyd – Transatlantic XTRA 5013 (Amer.).

WHALER OUT OF NEW BEDFORD – Folkways FS 3850 (Amer.).

LEVIATHAN (Whaling Songs) – Topic 12 T 174 (Eng.).

A SAILOR'S LIFE, Derek Sergeant – Oak Records (Amer.).

CHANSONS DE BORD FRANÇAISES, Marcel Noble and his Bordee – Pathé ATX 109 (Fr.).

CHANSONS DE LA MER, Les Campagnons du Large – Part I, RCA F 130 003; Part II, RCA F 130 028 (Fr.).

QUAYSIDE SONGS, OLD AND NEW, Spinners – HMV CLP 1500 (Eng.).

WIND UND WELLEN – Fontana 661600 (Ger.).

DE LA MER DU NORD À LA BRETAGNE (Instrumental only) – Pathé AT 1057 (Fr.).

WINDY OLD WEATHER, Bob Roberts – Talking Books 2/1501/26 (Eng.).

THE BLACKBALL LINE – Topic T 8 (Eng.).

HIGH BARBAREE – Columbia 33 S 1103 (Eng.).

SAILORMEN AND SERVING MAIDS (Folksongs of Britain, Vol. 6) – Caedmon TC 1162 (Eng.).

The following recordings were produced since 1970 and should be easy to obtain from folk-music shops.

SEA SONGS AND SHANTIES – Topic Sampler no. 7 TPS 205 (Eng.).

ACROSS THE WESTERN OCEAN – Swallowtail ST 4 (Amer.).

WHALING AND SAILING SONGS, Paul Clayton – Tradition 1005 (Amer.).

OFF TO SEA ONCE MORE – Stinson SLP 81 (Amer.).

SONGS OF THE WHALERS, Song Spinners – Kiwi M 31-I (N.Z.).

SHIPSHAPE AND BRISTOL FASHION, Erik Ilott – Folks'le (Eng.).

AS WE WERE A-SAILING, The Critics Group – Argo ZDA 137 (Eng.).

WON'T YOU GO MY WAY?, Peter Bellamy and Louis Killen – Argo ZFB-37 (Eng.).

WHALING SONGS AND BALLADS, Paul Clayton – Stinson SLP 69 (Amer.).

MEN AND THE SEA, Stan Hugill and the Folk Tradition – City Museum, Bristol (Eng.).

SEA SHANTIES – Topic 12 TS 234 (Eng.).

THE VALIANT SAILOR (Songs and Ballads of Nelson's Navy) – Topic 12 T S 232 (Eng.).

FIFTY SOUTH TO FIFTY SOUTH, Louis Killen – South Street Seaport Museum SPT-102 (Amer.).

YE MARINERS ALL, The Critics Group – Argo ZDA 138 (Eng.).

SEAMEN'S INSTITUTE SING AT SOUTH STREET SEAPORT – Folkways FTS-32418 (Amer.).

A GARLAND FOR SAM, Sam Larner (fisherman) – Topic 12 T 244 (Eng.).

ALL AT SEA, The Yetties – Argo ZFB 86 (Eng.).

DINGLES REGATTA – Dingles DIN 301 (Eng.).

YOUNG TRADITION (Sampler) – TRA SAM 13 (Eng.).

SCHELDELOODSENKOOR ZINGT SEA-SONGS EN SHANTIES – BMG SS 2418 (Holl.).

SCHELDELOODSENKOOR ZINGT SEA-SONGS EN SHANTIES – Mirasound SP 162 (Holl.).

VISA PÅ STORLUKA (Gamle Seilskuteviser) – TNLP 26 (Swed.).

DIE KNURRHAHNE – Brilliant HLP 10259 (Ger.).

SHANTIES (und Lieder von der Waterkant) – Europa E 157 (Ger.).

LIEDER VON DER WATERKANT, Shantychor-Cuxhaven – Baccarola 89216 ZT (Ger.).

CHANSONS SALÉES DE LA MARINE À VOILES – Disques Vogue SLD 735 (Fr.).

SEEMANNSLIEDER UND SHANTIES, Die Hamburger Tearjacks – Mandolino 5-120 (Ger.)

SHANTIES VON DER WATERKANT, Der grosse Windjammer-Chor – Intercord 28 711-0 (Ger.)

ROLLING HOME, Chor und Solisten der Seekameradschaft Nordsee – Karussel, Gold-Serie 2652 038 (Ger.).

BIBLIOGRAPHY

Books containing sea songs and shanties, sealore, nautical histories, seamanship, sailor yarns, and sea customs.

Anderson, R., *Seventeenth Century Rigging* (Salem, 1927).

Anderson, R. and R.C., *The Sailing Ship* (London, 1947).

Anson, Peter F., *Fisher Folk Lore* (1965).

Arnoux, Guy, *Chansons de marin français au temps de la marine en bois* (Paris, 1918).

Ashley, C., *Whaleships of New Bedford* (Boston, 1929).

Ashton, John, *Real Sailor Songs* (London, 1891).

Baltzer, R., *Knurrhahn* (Kiel, 1936; shortened reprint, Hamburg, 1952).

Beckett, Mrs. Clifford, *Shanties and Forebitters* (London, 1914).

Beckett, Comdr. W.N.T., *A Few Naval Customs, Expressions, Traditions and Superstitions* (Portsmouth, 1920).

Boughton, Capt. George P., *Seafaring* (London, 1926).

Bowen, F.C., *From Carrack to Clipper* (London, 1948).
—, *Sea Slang* (London, 1929).

Brochmann, D.H., *Opsang fra Seilskibstiden* (Christiana, 1916).
—, *Shantimanden* (Christiana, 1908).

Bullen, Frank T., and W.F. Arnold, *Songs of Sea Labour* (London, 1914).

Burney, Capt. C., *The Young Seaman's Manual and Rigger's Guide* (London, 1876).

Chapelle, H.I., *History of American Sailing Ships* (Reprint, New York, 1970).

Chapman, F.H. af., *Architectura Navalis Mercatoria* (Facsimile, Magdeburg, 1957).

Chovin, *Chansons de marins* (Paris, n.d.).

Clark, Capt, A.H., *The Clipper Ship Era* (London, 1910).

Colcord, Joanna C., *Songs of American Sailormen* (New York, 1938).

Course, Capt. A.G., *Windjammers of the Horn* (London, 1969).

Dana, R.H., *Two Years Before the Mast* (New York, 1840, and many times since).

Davis J., and Ferris Tozer, *Sailor Songs or "Chanties"* (London, 1887).

Doerflinger, W.M., *Shantymen and Shantyboys* (New York, 1951).

Falconer, W., *Universal Dictionary of the Marine,* 1780 (Facsimile, Newton Abbot, 1970).

Favara, Alberto, *Canti della terra e del mare di Sicilia* (Milan, 1948).

Granville, W., *A Dictionary of Sailors' Slang* (1962).

Harlow, F.P., *Chanteying Aboard American Ships* (Salem, 1948).

Hayet, Capt. A., *Chanson de bord* (Paris, 1927).
—, *Dictons et tirades des anciens de la voile* (Paris, 1934).

Höver, Otto, *Von der Galiot zum Fünfmaster* (Norderstedt, 1975).

Hugill, Stan, *Shanties from the Seven Seas* (London, 1961).
—, *Sailortown* (London, 1967).
—, *Shanties and Sailors' Songs* (London, 1969).

Jal, A., *Glossaire nautique* (Paris, 1848).

Jensen, Capt. Oscar, *Internationale Sømands-Opsange* (Copenhagen, 1923).

Jobe, J., *Great Age of Sail* (Lausanne, 1967).

Landström, Björn, *The Ship* (1961).

Laughton, L.C. Carr, *Old Ships, Figureheads and Sterns* (1925).

Le Bihor, Jean-Marie, *Chansons de la voile, "sans voiles"* (Dunkerque, 1935).

Lloyd, C., *The British Sailor* (London, 1968).
—, *Sea Fights Under Sail* (London, 1970).

Lubbock, B., *The Last of the Windjammers,* 2 vols. (Glasgow, 1927).
—, *The China Clippers* (Glasgow, 1929).
—, *The Down Easters* (Glasgow, 1930).

Masefield, J., *Sea Life in Nelson's Time* (London, 1905).

Mikkelsen, Børge, *Sømandssange, gamle og nye* (Copenhagen, 1941).

Nordhoff, Charles, *Nine Years a Sailor* (Cincinnati, 1857).

Olmstead, F.A., *Incidents of a Whaling Voyage* (New York, 1841).

Paasch, Capt., *Illustrated Marine Encyclopaedia* (Antwerp, 1890; Hamburg, 1901).

Pallman, Gerhard, *Seemannslieder* (Hamburg, 1938).

Patterson, J.E., *The Sea's Anthology* (New York, 1913).

Rappoport, Dr. A.S., *Superstitions of Sailors* (1928).

Sampson, John, *The Seven Seas Shanty Book* (London, 1927).

Schulz, G.T., *Unter Segeln Rund Kap Hoorn* (Hamburg, 1954).

Sharp, Cecil J., *English Folk-Chanteys* (London, 1914).

Shay, Frank, *Iron Men and Wooden Ships* (New York, 1924).

Smith, C. Fox, *A Book of Shanties* (London, 1927).

Smith, Laura A., *The Music of the Waters* (London, 1888).

Smyth, Adm. W.H., *The Sailor's Word-book* (London, 1867).

Spengemann, Friedrich, *Die Seeschiffe der Hannoverschen Weserflotte* (Norderstedt, 1975?).

Sternvall, Capt. S., *Sång Under Segel* (Stockholm, 1935).

Strobach, H., and Jens Gerlach, *Shanties* (Berlin, 1972).

Suscinis, Jean, *Chansons de la mer et de la voile* (Paris, n.d.).

Tegtmeier, K., *Alte Seemannslieder und Shanties* (Hamburg, n.d.).

Terry, R.R., *The Shanty Book* (London, 1931).
—, *Salt Sea Ballads* (London, 1931).

Underhill, H.A., *Masting and Rigging* (Glasgow, 1969).

Villiers, A.J., *The Way of a Ship* (London, 1954).

Whall, Capt. W.B., *Sea Songs and Shanties* (Glasgow, 1927).

Wossidlo, R., *Reise, Quartier in Gottesnaam* (Rostock, 1969).

Young, A., *Nautical Dictionary* (1846).

Oslo Sjømannsforening, Oslo, Norway
(for Norwegian shanties)

The late Comdt. Armand Hayet, Capitaine au Long-Cours, Paris
(French shanties)

Hans Sikorski Ltd., Hamburg
(for German shanties and songs)

Albert Bonnier Förlag, Stockholm, and Capt. S. Sternvall
(for Scandinavian songs and shanties)

Herbert Jenkins, London
(for British songs)

Routledge and Kegan Paul, Ltd., London
(for British shanties)

SPIN, Liverpool
(for various British and American songs and shanties)

G. Ricordi & Co., London and Milan
(for Sicilian songs)

Mr. Kees Hos, Assendelft, Holland, and Mr. Koen Suyk, Vereniging van Nederlandse Kaap Hoorn, Vaarders
(for Dutch songs and shanties)

Comdt. Le Maître, Antwerp

GLOSSARY

ABAFT: Aft of, behind, or at the rear.

ABOUT SHIP AND REEF TOPS'LS IN ONE: With the wind ahead a sailing ship has to proceed on a zigzag course, sailing with the wind on one bow for a certain distance (a *board*), then crossing the wind to bring it on the other bow. The master gives the order "About ship!," the men rush to their stations, haul and slack braces, the helmsman puts the wheel down, and the ship is brought on to a new tack. In the Old Navy, when reefing, the three big tops'ls would be lowered a little, the reef-tackles hauled on (so as to shorten the area of sail exposed to the wind), and the men would race aloft to "pass the earrings" and tie the reef-points – a "pleat" of sail having been hauled up to the yard to make a new or temporary head to the shortened sail. After the close of the Napoleonic Wars, in the so-called fancy frigates of the British Navy, in order to keep the men active and fit (in peacetime) these two maneuvers were performed together as a drill, three watches of men racing against each other on different masts.

ADVANCE-NOTE: A piece of paper worth a month's pay, handed to the sailor when he signs on a ship, which can be turned into cash by one of the sailor's relatives after his ship has sailed. In actual fact the sailor would hand the note to a crimp, boarding-house master, or ship chandler, these "gentlemen" cashing it for him at an usurious rate. The reduced amount he received would then buy him some shoddy clothing from the chandler, but more usually would be splashed on women and booze in dives owned by the above "gentlemen."

ARMSTRONG'S PATENT: Sailor term covering muscular, non-mechanical labor.

BACK THE MAIN TOPS'L: Method in which a ship's progress is stopped; e.g., when waiting to pick up a pilot. The yards and sails on the foremast and mizenmast are left as they are, full of wind, while those on the mainmast are swung in such a manner that the wind forces the sails *against* the mast and thereby impedes the ship's progress.

BEATING TO WIND'ARD: The same as tacking – trying to sail a ship forward against a head wind by zigzagging.

BLUENOSE: A general nautical term for Canadians, but more especially for Nova Scotian sailing ships and men.

BLUE PETER: A blue flag with an oblong white center, indicating a ship is about to sail when hoisted, at different periods, at the foremast or mainmast. Its name is said to derive from the French verb *partir*, to leave; or from Sir Peter Parker (1793), Admiral Cornwallis, known as "Billy Blue"; a corruption of "blue pierced"; or from "peter," an old name for a cabin trunk. Take your pick!

BLOODBOAT: The name applied to the Down Easter "hell-ships" that hailed from the Eastern American seaboard and engaged in the Cape Horn trade, whose masters and mates were all "buckos" or "bullies." The Down Easter *Gatherer* was the most infamous.

BOBSTAY: A steel bar, chain, or rope tackle from the end of the bowsprit to the waterline of the bow, preventing the bowsprit from lifting upward.

BRIGHTWORK: Includes the varnished teak pinrails around a ship inside the gunwales, the fiferail at the foot of each mast, companionway ladder handrails, teak railings around the poop, skylights, and poop "benches" – all having to be sanded and canvassed and scraped and varnished at least once a voyage by the seamen until, in smart ships, they "shone like silver." Also a ship's brass or chrome metalwork that required polishing.

BUCKO: A prefix often found in sailor-songs and stories indicating a tough mate or master. Probably introduced into sailor talk by way of the Irish packet rats.

CACHALOT: The sperm whale, hunted mainly by Yankee whalers in the South Pacific. This name comes from the French word *cache*, "box," which itself is the name given to a small bony section of the whale's head containing spermaceti, the precious oily substance used for making candles, ointments, and cosmetics. The English-speaking whaleman called this a "case," and because it was often a difficult place from which to extract the oil it was sometimes called a "hard case." The man engaged in extracting it also became known as a "hard case" and so the term entered the English language for someone who is considered tough.

CHAINS, CHAINPLATES: Metal bars or chains, extensions of the shrouds and backstays, which are fastened to a sailing-ship's sides beneath the channels, or wooden ledges, which spread the lower end of the rigging. A small boat coming alongside a ship would hook on to these chains so that passengers could climb aboard.

CHALK A SCORE: In sailortown pubs it was a common thing for a known sailor customer to be allowed credit, and what he owed for a night's drinking would be chalked up on a blackboard behind the bar.

CHESSTREE: In olden times a post, heavily carved, with a sheave in it through which the tack (rope) from the corner of the mainsail would be rove. In later ships this was merely a sheave in the ship's bulwark or side. (Sometimes written as *chesstress*.)

CHIP OFF THE OLD BLOCK: A name applied to the offsprings of a father who was a "bit o' a character," especially if they possessed his ways and looks.

CHIPPY, CHIPS: Sailor nickname for a ship's carpenter or shipwright.

CRACKERHASH: Biscuits broken into pieces and baked with small portions of salt beef or pork.

CRIMP: A person who procures men to serve as sailors or soldiers by tricking or coercing them.

DANDYFUNK: Biscuits pulverized with a belayin' pin (after being put in a canvas bag), the resultant mass being smeared with slush left over from the boiling of salt beef and baked in the galley oven (if permitted by the cook) in a cut-down bully tin.

DEAD-EYES: Blocks without sheaves, each with only three holes through which lanyards are rove. They are used to set up shrouds and backstays at the channels (outboard).

DOGSBODY: 1. Sea biscuits soaked in water to a pulp with added sugar. 2. A general factotum.

DONKEY'S BREAKFAST: This was the sailor name for the straw-stuffed bag of hessian which up to the Second World War was the only sleeping paillasse used by merchant seamen. It is even referred to in an early sea-ballad of 1400: "A sak of strawe were there right good." As the seaman headed toward his ship on sailing day, with a seabag over one shoulder, he would call on a dockside chandler, buy his donkey's breakfast, and hitch it up over his other shoulder. If it were pouring with rain, he'd sleep that night on its sodden straw, and before the voyage was over the straw would have wormed itself into great knotted lumps and possibly become the home of vicious bed-bugs.

DROGHER: A name given to wooden sailing ships in certain trades; e.g., sugar drogher, timber drogher, cotton drogher, etc.

DUKES: Slang name for "fists."

FIFERAIL: A teak rail around three sides of a mast, at its foot, pierced with holes to take the belayin' pins to which the sail cordage is "belayed" or fastened.

FLOGGING AROUND THE FLEET: A punishment for mutiny, insubordination, and desertion carried out in the British and other navies for over 400 years. The victim would be lashed to capstan bars laid athwart the launch, the latter proceeding around all the ships in the harbor, the man being flogged at each gangway until he had had his quota of lashes – up to 300 in extreme cases.

FOOTROPE: A two-inch rope served over with a tarry line called "spunyarn," stretched from one yardarm to the other and kept up to the after side of the yard by short lengths of ropes called "stirrups." In latter-day ships these footropes were made of wire. The seamen stood on them when reefing or furling the sails.

FUTTOCKS: A short ladder leading from the head of the lower shrouds to the edge of the top, difficult to climb back over. In fighting ships there was an opening in the top called a "lubber's hole," through which beginners and cowards would crawl, thereby dodging the cliff-hanging chore of mounting the futtock rigging.

FUFU BAND: A ship's "orchestra" in the days of sail. Although often including normal instruments – a melodeon, concertina, banjo, fiddle, and/or guitar – at times it would be made up of little more than a fiddle formed from a Havana cigar box, a penny whistle, a paper and comb, a drum shaped from an old paint tin with its top

and bottom removed and replaced with pig bladder skins (obtained from the galley if the cook was amicable), and the stamping of the men.

GUNWALE, GUNNEL: The upper edge of the bulwark or wall around the ship's sides, which in men-o'-war was pierced for guns. Gunwale is a corruption of "gun-wall."

HAIR CUT SHORT: Yankee seamen always preferred their hair cut "short back and sides," decrying the English and continental sailor fashion of the queue or pigtail.

HALF-SEAS-OVER: Half-drunk.

HARDTACK: Sea biscuit.

HILO: A word cropping up in many shanties, possibly the Peruvian port of Ilo, or the Hawaiian port of Hilo, or just simply the expression "high-low."

HOLYSTONE: A sandstone used by seamen to scrub and whiten the decks. A sailor yarn runs: In the eighteenth century ships of both the British Navy and the East India service used to anchor off Bembridge, Isle of Wight, in the St. Helen's Roads. Ashore here they could get good drinking water for their casks. The sailors discovered that the nearby ruined St. Helen's church contained blocks of sandstone which were good for cleaning the decks – hence the name "holystones." Large stones were called "bibles" and the smaller ones – which would be used by the seamen kneeling – "prayer-books."

HOOSEGOW: On the West Coast of South America jails were called in the Spanish tongues *juzgados.* Sailing-ship seamen who spent a lot of time behind bars called them, phonetically, "hoosegows," and from the Spanish spelling, "jughouses."

HOOSIERS: Cotton stevedores who worked on the wharves and levees of New Orleans and Mobile. The majority were black, but after the 1840s Creoles and white sailors who "screwed cotton" were also referred to by this name.

JOLLYBOAT: A general purpose ship's boat, its name probably stemming from the seventeenth-century name for a small boat – "gellywatte."

KEELHAULING: A severe naval punishment for desertion in which the victim was hauled from one yardarm to the other under the keel of the ship. The victim rarely sur-

vived; he would either be cut to ribbons by the shellfish on the ship's bottom or else become bloated with sea water.

LAZARET: Usually a room where old rope and so on is stowed aboard ship, but originally the ship's sick-bay. The word comes from *lazaretto,* a leper asylum in Near Eastern countries, which in turn comes from the place-name Nazareth.

LONGSPLICE: Sailor slang for marriage.

MUDHOOK: This and "killick" are sailor slang words for an anchor.

PACKET RATS: This was the name given to the tough seamen who manned the Western Ocean (Atlantic) packet ships running between Liverpool, New York, and Boston in the second and third decades of the nineteenth century. They were Irishmen hailing from New York, Liverpool, or Ireland herself. They were, in the main, great drinkers and singers, but awkward customers to handle. They were good seamen, too – with such men aboard a master could leave the shortening of sail until the last moment and be certain that these sailormen would be out and up aloft in a brace o' shakes and in no time have the sails muzzled and stowed. On the other hand, they weren't "fancy" sailormen, like the men of the clippers; i.e., they weren't interested in "sailorizing" – the arts of splicing, knotting, sewing canvas, and so on.

PRIVATEERS: Fighting ships in times of peace which were given "Letters of Marque" by their respective governments, permitting them to attack and sink ships of non-friendly countries without actually declaring war. In most cases such ships were no more than pirates.

ST. HELENA SOGER: To call a seaman a "soger" or "soldier," casting aspersions on his seamanlike qualities, was one of the worst epithets one could use in the days of sail. Shortly after the execution of Admiral Byng and the French taking of Minorca from Britain (1756), other derogatory epithets came into use among naval seamen – e.g., "Port Mahon soger" and "Port Mahon baboon."

SALT HORSE: Salt beef. On account of its stringlike qualities it was also known as "junk," a name for a certain type of bulrush from which rope was made in ancient times.

Because it was kept in a barrel called a "harness cask," there arose the idea of the "horse" in its "harness."

SNIFTERS: Savage squalls met off the coast of Tierra del Fuego.

SPLICE THE MAIN BRACE: The order given in the British Navy when issuing an extra tot of rum after a blow or sea fight. No really plausible theory has been put forward regarding the origin of the phrase.

SPRUNG: A word used at sea when a mast or yard has split or partly broken.

STOPPERS: Chains keeping the anchor to the cathead. There were two kinds – the "bow stopper" holding the ring of the anchor to the cathead, and the "shank painter" keeping the fluke (arm) of the anchor close to the ship's side. A bow stopper was also a rope or ropes preventing the huge anchor cable (rope) from running outboard.

TICKET-O'-LEAVE MEN: Convicts permitted a certain amount of parole, but not allowed to leave the country, especially in the case of those from the penal settlements of Van Diemen's Land (now Tasmania).

TIP THE CHINK: To issue grog to the men.

TOGS: Cant word for clothes, usually secondhand.

WHACK: After the Merchant Shipping Act of 1845, with its food allowance tables for seamen, sailors would demand their "whack" or full amount of food from the master if they thought they were being given short rations.

YARDARM: The outer end of a yard and not all the yard, as is often suggested nowadays by so-called authorities. It is the part from which a mutineer was hung.